To Betty with
love

Eden.

Kyra Novacz was a mystery to Bob Lundy. Where did she come from? Where was she going? And where had he seen her before? As his wife, Susan, put it: "You really don't know anything about her, do you . . . ?"

Bob liked Kyra, even though she was not a pretty girl. She was such a good listener and she was so helpful in re-typing the play he had written years ago. But he didn't expect to fall in love with her. He was surprised when he did and even more surprised when he found that Kyra could contemplate murder as the easiest way out of a desperate situation.

Kyra was a corrupting influence. In the primordial part of Bob's own mind — the part that is older than morality — he himself began to realize that murder was the easiest way out of a dilemma that was almost intolerable.

When murder was committed, it looked deceptively simple. One of those cases where suspicion asks not "Who?" but "Which?" Police and prosecution soon found that they could not answer that question beyond a reasonable doubt. The case was all the more baffling because the number of suspects was so limited.

Helen McCloy shows her accustomed skill when she solves the mystery with a surprise that does no violence to her characterizations. Her story combines a puzzle, logical to the last chapter, with portraits of contemporary human beings whose response to tragedy touches our emotions. This combination is as rare as it is welcome and Miss McCloy is to be congratulated on her seventeenth mystery novel.

Previous Books by Helen McCloy

Before I Die

Helen McCloy

A Torquil Book

Distributed by
DODD, MEAD & COMPANY
NEW YORK

To Elizabeth McCloy Hathaway,
With love from her cousin and friend

BEFORE I DIE

CHAPTER ONE

It ALL BEGAN that September day when Bob came back after lunch to the cell he called an office and found a memo on his desk.

Mr. Dorfmann wants to see you immediately.

As Dorfmann was a partner in the advertising agency, his office filled an eighth of the whole floor space, with windows on two sides. It was done in sober, masculine greys, relieved only by a movable bar in yellow leather and chromium.

"Hi, Bob! Where you been? We got trouble and I don't mean maybe. Lou Symington and her new husband are landing at Idlewild this afternoon."

"Jesus! Does she have to come East so soon again?"

"You know Lou. She does as she pleases."

"But —"

"She insists she's going to shoot her new picture here on location."

"Just one interview with New York reporters now and she'll wreck her career. The bitch!"

"Sure, she's that and every other bad word you can think of, but she's also a Valuable Property. She represents God-knows-how-many million dollars to Tantamount Pictures, our most important client. She's made a dirtier mess on the rug than usual this time, but it's our job to sweep it under the sofa and make the public believe she's a sweet, simple, young girl, who just needs a little more love and understanding."

"That's a tough assignment."

"You're telling me?"

"It can't be done. Not this time."

"It's got to be done this time."

"How about this one: *Lou is a great artist. She cannot be judged by ordinary standards. Crazed by the death of her second husband, she needed love desperately and found it with —*"

"The husband of her best friend? That's murder at the box office. I know because we've tried it already. Haven't you any new ideas?"

"Give me a minute."

Dorfmann glanced at the sweep hand of his watch. "You got sixty seconds." He picked up a press release and began to read.

Bob's mind raced the sweep hand. Louise Symington, born Hilde Pfeffer, had the dark, delicate face of a Murillo angel and the soul of a piranha fish that strips the flesh from the bones of its living victim in a few seconds. When she first appeared as a child actress, in a stage revival of *Dear Brutus*, there was not a dry eye in the house when she looked up into the baby-spot at the end of the second act, and whispered, with a catch in her voice: "Daddy . . . I don't want to be a might-have-been. . . ."

At twenty she was already a Valuable Property. But, unlike real estate and bonds and other valuable properties, she was also a human being and not a particularly nice one. Her first marriage and divorce didn't bother her fans. She was young and inexperienced, there were no children involved on either side, and the aging male star who had caught her went on to other conquests. Her second marriage, to a prominent director, seemed like true romance by the time Bob and Dorfmann's other copywriters got through with it. The adventures of the pair were followed with devout interest in all the fan magazines. But the second husband ran his sports car into a canyon one night, when he was coming home from a poker game in Hollywood with only a little blood in his alcohol stream. Lou had no intention of remaining a widow and this time her vagabond fancy fell on Dick Grant, Tantamount producer, and husband of Lou's closest friend, Gloria Wayne, another young actress, who was the mother of three small children.

Even then, if everything had been turned over to Dorfmann's boys, the divorce and remarriage might have been handled so blandly that the public would not have realized all that was going on. But Lou was thoroughly spoiled by this time. She honestly believed that she could get away with anything.

She and Dick stayed openly at the same hotel in New York. Gloria, besieged by reporters at Malibu, was so unprepared that she denied everything. Dick had to call Gloria then and tell her that he wanted a divorce. The reporters caught Gloria again in Reno, where she admitted, with tears, that it was all true and that she hadn't known anything about it when she gave her first interview. Lou and Dick, alighting from a plane at Los Angeles airport, made the mistake of boasting to reporters about their mutual bliss and adding a few tart comments about Gloria's selfishness in delaying their happy union.

All this had happened many times before in Hollywood, but this was the first time it had ever happened in public. That was a little too much, even for fans. The receipts at the box office began to fall off whenever a Lou Symington picture was shown, and it didn't help at all when the publicity department at Magna Films, which had Gloria under contract, began running tear-soaked articles in all the fan magazines making Gloria sound like the persecuted heroine of a soap opera. But Magna had to do something to salvage Gloria and they could hardly present her as an irresistible sex kitten after her husband's public desertion.

Politely venomous letters were exchanged between Tantamount Pictures in Hollywood and Kincaid, Kinsolving, Dorfmann and Viviani in New York. K., K., D. and V. pointed out that all Lou's interviews had been given without their knowledge or consent and they were, therefore, not responsible for the bad publicity. Tantamount replied in rolling, bureaucratic periods which, boiled down and translated, meant: "Don't let that bitch off the leash again!"

"Okay, minute's up!" said Dorfmann. "Any ideas?"

"Christ, I can't think of a thing! How can you whitewash a wench like that?"

"You musta known she'd break loose sooner or later after this third marriage," said Dorfmann. "You shoulda been working on an angle all this week."

"The trouble is the public knows too much," responded Bob. "Usually we're just hushing up some things they don't know. But this time, we've got to hush up some things they do know. We can't say it didn't happen, because everybody knows it did. Lou and Gloria were friends, Lou's husband kicks off and Lou decides she wants Gloria's, so she takes

Dick away from Gloria and the kids. Lou and Dick don't bother to tell Gloria until they are caught together by reporters in New York. Now that may be jake in the San Fernando Valley, or even on Park Avenue, but it's not jake in Pratt Falls, Iowa, and this whole country is Iowa outside New York and southern California. So...."

"So what?"

"Wait a minute." Bob closed his eyes like a poet communing with his muse. "I think I've got something. What is there that we *can* change? We *can't* change the fact that Lou stole Gloria's husband. We *can't* change the fact that Dick and Lou let Gloria learn the news publicly from reporters. We *can't* change the fact that Gloria has three cute-looking babies."

"If only it weren't for those kids!" moaned Dorfmann, in real distress. "Why do they have to be so cute? Why couldn't they be spastic or something? And why do the fan mags keep showing pictures of them?"

"Because their mother's under contract to Magna." Bob pointed out patiently. "But listen, Dorf. There's one thing we *can* change. Just one."

"There is?"

"Sure. We can get an interview with some has-been actor, or actress, who knew both families, and who will do anything for a buck and we can make this has-been say ..." Bob paused for emphasis, then assumed his fan-mag voice — a sugary, almost prim falsetto: " 'Lou and Gloria were never really friends at all.' "

There was a moment's hush as Dorfmann sat utterly still, awed by this daemonic inspiration. Then:

"Boy, I wonder if that would work?"

He closed his eyes in turn and leaned his head against the back of his chair. Now he, too, was speaking like a sybil in

trance. "I can see it in print. Of course. *The two husbands
were friends, a producer, a director. They liked to talk shop
and play poker together. But I honestly can't remember ever
having seen Gloria and Lou together more than two or three
times and, even then, it was always at some crowded public
gathering, at Mr. Goldwyn's or Mr. Zanuck's. After all, the
two women had very little in common. Gloria is a sweet girl,
but not an actress of the same caliber as Lou, who is so devoted to her art. Gloria was always thinking of her home and
children. Lou, to her great regret, has never had children and
so her whole life is centered in her art. If they had been close
friends, I surely would have known it, because I was very
intimate with both families.* . . . And so on and on and on and
on. Is the public that dumb?"

"You cannot aim too low," quoted Bob cheerfully. "The
only thing we can change in this whole situation is the as-
sumption that Lou and Gloria were close friends, but, if you
can change that, you change everything."

"It's a pretty big 'if.' It might backfire. It might get us all in
trouble."

"I don't see how it could. We can throw a cocktail party
for Lou and Dick at the Waldorf this afternoon when they
get in. Have all the columnists there, and plant the idea right
away. I'll meet them at Idlewild and tell Lou she's got to lay
off the liquor for an hour or so and try to look and act the way
she does on the screen. Hell, if she can seduce a hundred and
sixty million fans on film, she ought to be able to seduce a
hundred and sixty half-soused reporters in the flesh."

"It's risky."

"What else can we do?"

"Okay, we'll gamble, but if we lose, you're out of a job. Tell
Lou to look tragic and terribly in love, the way she did in that
movie about Pearl Harbor. Didn't she have a fall on the set

ten days ago? Say she injured her chest muscles, or her back, and she's come East primarily to see a doctor. Take shots of her looking at Dick, when he doesn't know she's looking at him. That lovely pan of hers lends itself to timid, wistful devotion. By the way — were they friends?"

"Gloria and Lou? Of course. The best of friends. It was Gloria who got Lou her first break in Hollywood six years ago."

Dorfmann sighed. "Have you ever stopped to think that this is a helluva way to earn a living?"

"Often. Yet there are dopes who would think it fun to work alongside a glamour-puss like Lou Symington."

"They wouldn't if they knew Lou like you and I know Lou. . . . When I was a little kid I wanted to be a fireman. There are times when I wish I had."

"I always wanted to be a playwright," said Bob. "I even got as far as writing a play."

"And then?"

"I got married."

"So did I," said Dorfmann. "A fireman's pay wouldn't keep my wife in nylons."

Bob had a sudden sense of disloyalty to Sue. "Aren't we making scapegoats out of our wives? If you'd really wanted to be a fireman, and if I'd really wanted to be a playwright, we'd have managed it somehow, married or not."

"*Moon and Sixpence* stuff?"

Bob nodded. "Sue's never held my nose to the grindstone. I did it myself. Maybe that makes it worse."

Dorfmann sighed again. "Funny how you don't really mind the grindstone when you're twenty or thirty or forty. But when you hit fifty, you suddenly look around and think: 'God! There's no way to go but down!' "

"You feel that way, too?" Bob was surprised. "It hit me right after my fiftieth birthday. I suddenly realized I've never been anywhere, I've never done anything and nothing has ever happened to me. The kind of things that happen to people in books. And now nothing ever will happen to me. I'll just go on, commuting from Westchester to New York, and making enough money to pay bills and taxes. My life is a story without a plot."

"The rats in the maze — that's us," said Dorfmann. "But who's running this ghastly experiment? And why?"

Bob rose. "I'd better get on the phone to the Waldorf." At the door, he paused. "You know what I want, Dorf?"

"A raise."

"No, an adventure. Just one real adventure. Before I die."

Dorfmann looked at Bob shrewdly. "Sexual adventure?"

"I don't believe the word adventure means only that. It means something exciting, improbable, unpredictable and dangerous."

Dorfmann's laugh was loud. "What could be more exciting, improbable, unpredictable and dangerous than sex? That's what you want, boy, whether you know it or not!"

CHAPTER TWO

LOU WAS FIRST off the plane, bareheaded and swathed in yards of precious fur, clutching a jewel case in one small, predatory hand. She was not at her best. Her fur stole was too warm for the mild September day and her face was greasy with sweat. She was hatless and the wind touselled her short, black hair, while the sun sought out the first faint lines around her mouth, the first hint of bags under her eyes — flaws that lighting and camera angles glossed over when she was on screen. She hadn't bothered to re-powder her nose. It was shiny and slightly red.

"Miss Symington!" shrilled a female reporter. "I just want to ask you if —"

Bob ran interference smoothly. "Miss Symington is here primarily to see her doctor. She had a serious fall on the set recently and strained the muscles of her chest. She'll be glad to see any of you in her suite at the Waldorf later this afternoon, but, after this exhausting trip, she must have rest. At least an hour or so. Please let us pass."

He had taken Lou's arm and squeezed it gently, a hint that she was to pick up this cue. She gave him a mutinous side glance and turned toward the reporters. She was checked by the hostility in their eyes.

"Please . . ." It was the velvet voice they had all heard on the sound-track. "I'm so tired . . ."

Her husband moved in on her other side, trailed by her maid. She accepted escort meekly until they were all in the car, rolling toward New York.

"What the hell is all the God damned fuss about?" she then demanded. "You'd think nobody in the United States had ever married a divorced man before!"

"I'd like you to read this press release," said Bob. "It'll show you the line we think you ought to take."

"Let me see it." Dick took the script. His face relaxed as he read. He was smiling by the time he handed it on to Lou.

"Take a gander at this, baby. These boys at K., K., D., and V. are smart and I think you should play along with them. You didn't like those last box office reports any more than the studio did."

Lou glanced at the script perfunctorily and tossed it on the floor. "Okay, if you say so, but such a fuss about nothing makes me want to puke. What I need now is a drink."

Patiently, tactfully, politely, Bob explained that she was to lay off liquor for just this one afternoon and try to look like a *femme fatale* touched by tragedy, aware that she had sinned, but redeemed by the fact that her sin was for love — pure, sweet, romantic love.

"What's all this jazz about my straining my chest muscles?"

"More malarkey to put you in good, kid," explained Dick.

"Okay, okay, anything for dear, old Tantamount."

The rest of the drive passed in sulky silence. Bob studied the pair covertly and wondered what they really saw in each other. Lou's youthful beauty was fading rapidly. She would be old at thirty. Dick was already in middle age — a bald spot, a paunch, heavy lines around a sagging, disillusioned mouth.

Was Dick just tired of wife and brats and domesticity? And flattered by the attention of a famous beauty, fifteen years younger than himself? Did Lou feel she must have a producer-husband to take over her business worries? Or was it something below the surface of life that they hardly understood themselves? Like Dick reminding Lou of the first boy she had ever kissed, or Lou happening to look like Dick's mother, who had died long ago. But why call it love? The homage vice pays to sentiment? Love was creative. Whatever blind and violent feeling these two had for each other, it had been destructive from the beginning.

Bob's thoughts strayed to his own life, Sue and the children. He didn't believe he would be able to stand his daily contact with this grimy world of sham, if he didn't have that other, cleaner world to go home to.

While Lou and Dick were dressing, Bob reviewed the arrangements for the party in the living room of their suite. "No dips and none of those hot frankfurters on toothpicks!" he told the floor-waiter sternly. "This is a swank party. We want creamed *foie gras* and black caviar and bay scallops with a very hot sauce and little cheese soufflés on toast rounds. And we want hot things hot and cold things cold. As for the drinks, hold it down to Martinis, champagne, scotch, rye, Bourbon and cognac. We don't want to spend too much money."

"There's someone at the door, sir," said the waiter. "Mr. Conrad Albany."

Bob hurried to the doorway. Conrad Albany was a real find

that Dorfmann had dug up at the last moment. He was a good bit better than a has-been for, though he had retired from starring roles in the movies, he appeared each week in his own TV show, a good reliable situation-comedy series that had been on the air for several years, *Dude Ranch*. Money alone would hardly induce such a man to spread the word that Lou and Gloria had never been friends, but Bob suspected that the fellow was really after a fat part in Lou's next picture. TV brings in a decent income, but does little to satisfy an actor's desire to act.

"Mr. Albany? I'm Bob Lundy of K., K., D. and V."

"Mighty pleased ta meetcha, son." Off-screen, as on, Conrad Albany was aggressively, professionally Western. He looked the part — weathered skin and lean body, tough as whipcord, eyes the clear blue of the Arizona skies with a faraway look, as if he kept them mostly on the horizon, a shock of untidy grey hair, as if he never bothered with these effete, new-fangled barber shops, but had ole Chang, the Chinese cook, clip the ends with sheep clippers when he got to lookin' like one o' these here Beatniks they got down Frisco way. And he acted the part. The dry, drawling voice that meticulously avoided all terminal G's and the finer points of grammar, and the eyes that twinkled in a deadpan face when he came up with some particularly shining gem of droll, homespun philosophy.

It was the first time Bob had met him, and there was only one thing to say: "You're exactly the way you seem on TV."

"Well, now, thank'ee, son. That there's a compliment, I reckon. Not a compliment to my actin', o' course. But I calc-late one reason *Dude Ranch* is such a big hit is just because folks is tired of these actin'-type actors. When they see Con Albany up there, on that li'l silver screen, they know he's for real. He's just what he seems — a tough, old cowhand, who's picked up a bit o' homely wisdom in his long, hard life an' so he's able to straighten out some o' them tenderfeet boys and gals what comes to stay at his *Dude Ranch*."

"You do understand why you are here this afternoon, Mr. Albany?"

There was an instant of shrewdness in the faraway blue eyes, but only an instant. He could not stop acting. "Call me Con, son, like everybody else does. Sure thing I know why I been roped into this here corral. My job is to help out a mighty purty li'l lady, Mis' Lou Symington, by puttin' the word around, jest casual-like, that she an' another mighty purty little lady never was friends like all these newspaper fellas been a-sayin' they was. Hell, I knowed them gals fur years and they wasn't never friends. Mis' Lou, all she cares about is her art and Mis' Gloria — well, she's more of a home-body, jest actin' fer money an' spendin' all her spare time with her kids. Two gals like that cain't never be pardners."

Lou paused on the threshold of her bedroom.

"Con Albany!"

"Well, honey-chile!" He spread his arms and she ran into them with every appearance of enthusiastic affection. Dick Grant winked at Bob, but Bob didn't see the wink. He was looking at his watch. He had reached that awful moment that precedes every cocktail party when the host is suddenly afraid that no one is coming.

Five minutes later the room was swirling with people, their high-pitched chatter bouncing off ceiling and walls. The shaded lamplight was kinder to Lou Symington than the sun, and her maid had worked wonders with creams and lotions and powders and rouge. Now her skin seemed like a peach, her eyes dewy as a girl of eighteen's. She wore black velvet,

low-cut, full-skirted, with a black lace mantilla over her hair.
No jewels, but a simple, gold wedding-ring. When her frail
hand drew the lace together across her throat, somehow you
thought of a pathetic beggar-maid, drawing a thin shawl about
her as protection against a cruel wind.

The photographers got a beautiful shot of her that way,
tragic and unsmiling, as she gazed at Dick. Con Albany
threaded his way deftly among reporters and magazine writers.
"Never saw Lou an' Gloria together all the time I knew 'em
... 'cept at some big shindig, like that garden party of my ole
pal, Zanuck's. ..." By the time the gang were on their third
round of drinks, there wasn't a man or woman in the room
who seemed to care a fig for Gloria's side of the story. Con's
bad grammar and slovenly enunciation carried immense conviction. Weren't these things traditional symbols of simple
honesty on and off screen? Dorfmann was wrong. The thing
couldn't backfire. Not as long as Lou stayed sober.

Something accomplished, something done, Bob had earned
a night's repose. But, first of all, he could stand a drink himself. He had stayed away from the bar until he was fairly sure
there would be no crisis. Now he thought he could risk one
drink. Just one.

Most of the crowd had drifted away from the bar to the
other end of the room, where Lou was serenely holding court.
Two or three, who never deserted any bar, were holding out
empty glasses to the barman, so Bob decided to help himself.
To reach the bar, he had to pass in front of a girl, who was
sitting on a window-sill, alone. He had noticed her earlier in
the afternoon, largely because she didn't speak to anyone and
no one spoke to her. He had felt sorry for her. She seemed so
completely friendless. Now that he looked at her more closely,
he had an odd feeling that he had seen her somewhere before.

She could hardly be called pretty. She was too big, too solid and meaty for that. Her cheeks were chubby, little balloons on either side of a sharp nose, and her eyes were small. She smiled at him as she moved her feet out of his way and her eyes disappeared behind her cheeks. Where the eyes had been, there were now just two little, crescent slits, edged with sandy lashes. Her mouth, too narrow for a real smile, formed another little crescent. Her smile was like one of those crude, stylized faces that children draw on cookies with three scallops of chocolate syrup.

Bob spoke first. "Ready for another drink?"

"Thank you." It was a tiny voice, a thin, grey, thread of sound, without inflection, the voice of a breathless child. There was nothing she could do to reduce the proportions of her big-boned body, but she could reduce the volume of her voice and, perhaps, that was an even more effective way to stimulate the paternal instincts of the male.

Bob filled her glass, lifted his own and said: "Cheers!"

That was the moment when he should have turned away from her, but it seemed churlish to leave her so abruptly, when she was so alone. "Enjoying the party?"

"Very much." She didn't elaborate and that was different from most women he knew. They would have gone on volubly to praise the food and the drinks and Lou Symington. This woman had the technique of a psychiatrist. She gave all her attention and then left the floor to him. Almost any man will rush in to fill a conversational vacuum as if he were afraid of unspoken thoughts.

"It's a damned good turn-out," said Bob. "But, of course, we have a drawing card — Lou. I'm Bob Lundy. I don't believe I know your name."

"I'm Kyra Novacz."

"I've a crazy feeling I've met you before, but I don't recognize the name."

"I'm sure I'd remember if we'd met before."

"Are you with a newspaper, or a magazine?"

"Neither." She set her glass down on the bar. "I just happened to be in the lobby today and I saw a crowd of people all flocking to one elevator, so I followed them up to this suite."

Bob had heard of young people who took advantage of the many business cocktail parties in New York hotels where the host cannot possibly know every guest by sight, but he had never visualized any of them like this one — so quiet, so passive and so unbelievably frank.

"Shocked?"

"No-o. But I'm afraid K., K., D., and V. would be."

"Who's K., K., D., and V.?" She sounded like a child repeating a long word without understanding it.

"My bosses. Kinsolving, Kincaid, Dorfmann and Viviani. Public Relations. They're throwing the party and I'm here to run it for them."

"Oh, dear, I did pick the wrong man to speak to! Are you going to throw me out?"

CHAPTER THREE

No MATTER WHAT she said, her voice never changed; it was always toneless, pale, pathetic. There was something irritating in presumption voiced so colorlessly. His rejoinder was tart.

"Can you think of one good reason why I shouldn't?"

"No." The voice was hardly audible.

Still he made no move to lead her towards the exit. "Do you often do this sort of thing?"

"No. I was just lonely. I'm often lonely."

"You live alone?"

"No, I live with my father. He's old and diabetic and needs a lot of care, so I don't have a regular job. I just help him with his typing and things like that."

"What does he do?"

"He's with the U.N. A translator. We come from one of those wretched little countries you never heard of that the

Habsburgs and Romanoffs have been fighting over for nearly
a thousand years."

"Who's got it now?"

"Nobody. We're supposed to be independent, like Austria,
but, of course, if there should be another war, we'll be right
in the middle."

"No, you won't. The ICBM's will whistle over your heads,
going in both directions, and, when we're wiped out, you'll be
sitting pretty. Let me freshen up your drink."

She smiled her funny smile as she held out her glass. "Then
you're not going to throw me out?"

"You knew I wouldn't. And you didn't pick me to speak to.
I picked you."

"But I smiled at you first. I never would have guessed you
were running this whole thing. You look much too young for
that. Do you know what I really thought? That you'd just
wandered in off the street the way I did!"

Bob laughed. There was something enormously appealing
about this girl once you got to talking to her. "You speak good
English for a foreigner," he said.

"Oh, we've been here a long time now, Dada and I. Soon
after the U.N. was founded."

"But you don't have any accent at all."

"Thank you." Again that droll smile. It was like her voice,
different, piquant, a personal signature that made her stand
out from other girls.

A heavy hand fell on Bob's shoulder. "Swell party, Boy, and
these releases will look great in tomorrow's papers!"

Bob swung around to respond to Dick Grant's tipsy cordi-
ality and discovered that the party was over. The room was
almost empty. Lou had kicked off her shoes, poured herself
a scotch so strong it was as dark as iced coffee, and curled up in

one corner of a sofa, was making up for lost time in her drinking. Dick had taken off his jacket and tie and opened his shirt collar. Con Albany sat astride a small chair, facing its back, where he rested his elbows. Everyone else had gone.

"Guess they thought Dick and I were giving the party," said Lou. "They all said good-bye to us."

"A mighty fine spread." Con reached a long arm out to a tray on an occasional table and scooped up three devilled eggs. "I sure enjoyed myself an' I spread the word around among them magazine-writin' gals, Mis' Lou. Effen I ain't mistook, you-all's goin' ter git some plum dandy write-ups, sugarfoot."

Bob looked at his watch. "I didn't realize it was so late, Dick. Guess I'll spend the night in town."

"Want a room here?" suggested Dick.

"No, thanks, I always stay at a small hotel near the office. May I use your phone?"

"Sure."

It took less than a minute to get through to Susan, now you could dial Westchester direct. "Hello, darling! I'm awfully sorry, but I got hung up tonight. Cocktail party for Lou Symington, who just flew in."

"Oh, Bob, that awful woman!"

"Yes," Bob said, loudly. "She's just as lovely as ever. I'm looking at her right now," he added so that Sue wouldn't think he had suddenly gone crazy.

Lou preened herself. Bob wondered what she would have done if she had heard Sue.

"It's so late now I'm going to spend the night in town."

"I did have such a lovely steak for you!" Sue's voice was a shade querulous. "And Robin made an apple pie."

"Too bad, honey, but it can't be helped. Tell Robin I'll

have some of her apple pie tomorrow. Kiss her and Buzz for
me."

"You know Buzz won't let anybody kiss him now!"

"Well, tell him from me he's a fool if he won't let his
mother kiss him. I'll be home tomorrow on the early train —
four-ten." Bob's voice dropped and softened. "Darling, I love
you very much!"

"Darling, I love you!" Susan hung up.

Both Lou and Kyra were looking at Bob with an entirely
new interest, as if he had suddenly come alive for them. Lou
spoke: "I believe you really do love that wife of yours."

"Sure I do." Bob laughed.

"How long have you been married?"

"Well, Robin's the elder and she was born in 1949, so we
were married in 1948. That's — good grief, it's fifteen years."

Lou and Dick looked at each other. "Wonder if ours will
last that long?"

"I know it will!" Lou's rich voice throbbed. "I have never
known love before. But this is the real thing."

"I'm sure glad to hear that," put in Con with fatherly concern. "You been switchin' yore pardners too often, honey-
chile. Now you-all got yourself a nice fella like Dick here,
y'oughter settle down an' hev some kids, like Bob an' me."

"Didn't even know you were married," said Lou.

"Oh, come on now! Everybody knows I've been married
to my li'l, cotton-pickin' wife for thirty-one years. Didn't I
ever show you a snap of my li'l grandson, Con, Jr.? Cutest li'l
tyke y'ever laid yer eyes on in all yer born days!"

Out came the wallet and the snapshot. Lou regarded the
toothless, bald-headed baby with an enthusiasm she had no
difficulty in controlling. She was interested in only the first
step of the reproductive process.

"May I see?" Kyra's shadow of a voice slid into the moment of silence gently. Con looked up, as if he were aware of her for the first time.

"You sure can!" He moved over to the sofa, where she was sitting, and sat beside her. He had to sit close so they could look at the picture together.

"How sweet!" Kyra's voice was hardly more than a whisper. "You're a lucky man."

"Always been kinda lucky." He smiled, his face close to hers, and laid one hand on her arm. "You're gonna be lucky, too, one o' these days, sugarfoot. You're gonna get you a nice young fella for a husband an' have a cute little tyke, jest about like Con, junior, here." His hand was stroking her arm by this time.

Why, the old goat! thought Bob. Wonder how many times he's been unfaithful to his li'l cotton-pickin' wife?

Gently, tactfully, Kyra twisted away from him, and rose. "I must be getting along. . . ."

"You've all got to eat somewhere," said Dick. "How about a snack with us here?"

If it hadn't been for that second scotch, Bob would have said: "No, thanks, I have a heavy day tomorrow. I'd better get back to my own hotel." But the whiskey was warm within him, Dick's invitation was well-meant and, what a break for this lonely little kid, Kyra Novacz, to have supper with three people whom she would undoubtedly regard as thrillingly celebrated — Lou, and Dick, and, to a lesser degree, even poor, old Con. Already he was thinking of Kyra's hundred and sixty-odd pounds as "little."

So there were more drinks and food — all kinds of food, *filet mignon,* and roast duck and a Rock Cornish game hen, and lobster. Who had ordered what? Nobody could quite remember by that time, so everybody had some of everything and then there was Irish coffee — lots of coffee, lots of whipped cream, and lots of Irish whiskey. Nobody was tight, of course, but everybody was mellow until, suddenly, it was very late indeed and time that Bob took Kyra home.

"You don't haveta, boy," said Con. "I'd be purely pleased and plumb tickled —"

"I'm taking her home." Bob's tone left no room for argument.

One of the doormen got them a taxi and Kyra gave Bob an address on Riverside Drive. He was sleepy and it was only natural that his head should rest on Kyra's shoulder. She didn't push him away, but neither did she encourage him. She just let his head lie there while she sat still, almost indifferent. An odd girl, always watching, waiting . . . for what?

He woke with a start to find her paying the cab driver. "Hey, this is on me!"

"That's all right. You must come in for a while. I'll make some coffee."

Bob shook his head and blinked until he could see her more clearly in the stagey spotlight of the street lamp. That smile of hers was damned cute. So were those chubby cheeks. Just a kid. He wondered if her buttocks were as chubby.

"Okay, honey, anything you say."

The taxi driver gave them a long, hard, cynical look as he pushed up his flag and swung back into traffic.

Bob followed high heels up five steps, through an open door into a vestibule with letter boxes. One of the boxes displayed a visiting card engraved: "Daniel Novacz." She had a latch key to unlock the inner door. They stepped into a dim hallway. "We're on the ground floor, what they call a garden apartment. My father hates climbing stairs." She was fitting another key into another door. She opened it and flipped a switch that brought light to shaded lamps.

Bob was vaguely aware of an old, high ceiling, a worn parquet floor, French windows facing the river, and a fireplace with a gas log. He took off his hat and sank gratefully on a sofa. "Where's your father?" The words were a little blurred.

"In Washington. A conference at the Legation. He won't be back until tomorrow afternoon."

"So you're all alone tonight?"

"Yes. Now you see why I was feeling so lonely this afternoon."

Bob was aware of strength in her — the hidden, terrible strength of weakness, the cold heart that preys on pity. *I must not pity her too much*, he thought drowsily. . . .

The next thing he knew she was beside him on the sofa with a cup of steaming coffee and a plate of rich, buttery coffee cake. He ate and drank and, in a few minutes, the drowsiness was gone.

She had changed when she went to make the coffee. Now she was wearing a housecoat of lime green satin that moulded her body in the ample curves of an amphora. One large, rhinestone button held the fastening in place. Just one.

Bob began to talk about himself — his stupid, disillusioning job, his nice wife, his cute children, the play he had always wanted to write.

"I could help." Kyra was sitting beside a desk, playing with a paperweight, a miniature anvil that looked as if it were made of bronze or iron. "I could do the typing for you. You could dictate to me, or to a tape recorder. It would give me something to do when Dada is at the U.N."

"Now that's an idea!" He was enthusiastic. "I hate typing. It's one thing that has held me back. All that typing and re-typing every time I revise."

"Oh, will you let me do it? Please!"

"You're darn tootin' I will. Oh, gosh, I sound like Con Albany, don't I? It must be contagious."

Kyra laughed. She was quick to catch a shade of meaning. A remarkably intelligent girl. The sort of girl who can really appreciate an intelligent, older man. He didn't know when he had passed a pleasanter evening.

At last his attention turned from himself, a subject he had fairly well exhausted, to the girl beside him. "I want you to meet Sue. You and she are sure to like each other. You must come out to our house and spend a week-end with us. That's one way you can meet young people. It's just not right for a girl like you to be cooped up in an apartment like this with no friends her own age."

"I'm used to it now and Dada needs me."

"He ought to think of your future. Don't you ever want to get married?"

"Of course. Every woman does. How can I be happy without a husband? But ... the way things are ..."

"You poor kid!" What man is not touched by woman's admission that only man can make her happy? "Would it do any good if I talked to your father?"

"I'm afraid not." Her eyelids dropped. "He's old-fashioned. The old country, you know. Marriages are still arranged by parents there. At least they were in his youth."

"But you're not in the old country. Hell, somebody ought to talk to him."

"Oh, Bob, that would only make it worse. Honestly!" He saw water in her eyes.

"You poor, little kid!" He was so moved he didn't know quite what to do, so he did the natural, human, fatherly thing — he put his arms around her and kissed her gently on the lips. They were warm and silken-smooth and her breath was sweet. He kissed her again, a little less fatherly this time. Her lips parted in response.

In a far corner of his mind, a sense of alarm stirred faintly as the sound of a distant bell. She lifted her arms up to circle his neck. The lifting movement put too great a strain on the threads that held the rhinestone button in place. It rolled across the floor and the long, green coat fell open. She wore nothing else.

It was a long time since he had seen the firm, rosy flesh of youth. It was a long time since he had known the potent stimulus of feminine pungency — the raw essence of youth and fertility, the smell of life itself. . . .

Only when it was too late did he begin to suspect that he might be in real trouble.

"Kyra, you don't understand. This must not happen again. I love my wife. I love my children. I don't want another family. I have a family. I'll never get a divorce."

"But —"

"Kyra, listen. I'm sorry for you. I'll do anything I can to help you. I want you to get out and meet people your own age. Some day I hope I'll dance at your wedding. But there is nothing real between us. There must be no misunderstanding about that. We're not going to hurt Sue and we're not going to hurt each other. We're going to be sensible and intelligent."

"But the play! I was going to help with your play!"

"We can still work together on the play. Why not? I'll send you the script tomorrow. You can make a clean copy — the old one is all marked up — and when I revise the new copy, I'll send you the revision to type for me. Listen. Nothing is changed. You can still come out to Westchester and meet Sue. What happened tonight was . . . an accident. It will never happen again and no one will ever know anything about it."

"But it did happen!"

"No. It never happened at all. And now I must go."

She stood at a front window with a fold of curtain drawn aside just far enough for her to see him without his being able to see her, if he should look back. But he didn't. He hesitated at the curb, as if he were looking for a taxi, then walked north towards the subway station.

She dropped the curtain and went back to the bedroom. She stood naked in front of a pier glass and studied herself intently. She had always used her body as a weapon and she was glad that it was a good one. After all, it was the only weapon she had.

She had just put on a nightgown and a terrycloth robe, when she heard a key in the lock. Her eyes changed. She ran into the living room, but she was too late. He was already standing in the doorway, looking at the two coffee cups. His hair was white, his eyes grey and sharp as needle points. He was leaning on an old fashioned, malacca stick.

"Dada! I didn't expect you so soon!"

"I dare say you didn't. The Minister decided to drive to New York. He gave me a lift. You are alone?"

"Of course!"

"But you haven't been alone long." His glance rested on the green housecoat, on the sofa where she had left it.

"Oh. . . . I was just mending it. The button fell off."

He lowered himself into an armchair slowly, laboriously, resting his stick between his knees.

"I would like my slippers and my pipe."

She hurried into a bedroom, came back with slippers. He stretched out a foot. She knelt beside him to unlace his shoe. "You are a good girl, Kyra, aren't you?"

She smiled up at him. "I was well brought up. I had a good father."

"Certainly you had one who taught you woman's place in the scheme of things . . . or tried to. Just because we are living in America now, you must not forget what you were taught."

"I won't."

She started to rise. His hand shot out and caught her arm in a vicious grip. "Liar! What have you been doing tonight that brings such stars into your eyes?"

"Nothing! Honestly, I —"

"Up to your old tricks again, aren't you?" He shook her arm violently. She wrested her arm free, struggled to her feet. He rose as she did.

"I will not stand for this, Kyra!" His arm moved and his stick flashed through the air. He brought it down with a resounding smack on her buttocks, once, twice. Screaming, she fled into her bedroom, but he was close behind. She turned to shut the door and he struck her across the face.

All the hatred in the world seemed to gather in her eyes. "I hate you! You're horrible and I hate you! Some day I'm going to kill you!"

CHAPTER FOUR

SUSAN LUNDY SAT at her dressing-table, brushing her hair, still damp from the shower. When the first salting of grey had appeared, she had asked Bob: "Shall I do something about it?" He had kissed her and laughed. "God, no! I love you because you're you, not just because of the color of your hair." A few years later, when she could no longer ignore the wishbone line on either side of her nose, she had said: "Facial exercises are slower than face-lifting, but cheaper." That time Bob had frowned. "For Pete's sake, Susan, those lines are a living record of all we've been through together. Let them alone."

From that time on, Susan looked at her face in the mirror with a pleasure that few younger women can know. Even the scars of age were reminders that she was that rarest of all human beings — a woman who loves and is loved in middle age. So strong was her feeling that she and Bob were among the fortunate few, who go through life unscathed by the great tragedies, that even when Buzz came down with polio, she was sure that he would get well again in a few months. Nothing really dreadful could happen to people who loved each other so much.

The day was cold, so she put on a wool dress, soft and clinging, in a subtle shade of red, as cozy as a wood-fire. She went downstairs with a light step, humming one of the songs of her youth. She had put up the Christmas wreaths that morning, when the *Times* reminded her that there were "only twenty-one shopping days till Christmas." They were the same wreaths she had used last year, made of shining balls set in evergreen, one red, one blue, one silver, and they sparkled festively against the pale walls. On each wreath perched the image of a dove with spread wings, its feathers as white as the new-fallen snow beyond the windows.

The front door opened as she reached the stair landing. Robin stood on the hemp mat, just outside, stamping snow off her rubber boots. She was named for her father, Roberta, and no one remembered now whether it was her baby-talk or Susan's mother-talk that had turned the name into Robin. "Hi, Mom!" Her greeting was always off-hand and awkward when she first got home from school, as if she had been so immersed in her own generation that she could not adjust to the wave-length of her elders immediately. Only in the evening, when she was getting ready for bed, would she forget the slang and the calculated air of indifference. Only then would Susan learn the news of her daughter's day.

Robin tossed her coat and scarf on a bench and stood before the hall mirror combing the shining curls that framed her face with such natural art that no one would have guessed she put them up in rollers every night. Her white shirt was like a boy's, with roll-up sleeves and button-down collar. She wore knee socks, a kilt and sneakers. That year only creeps left their hair straight and wore skirts instead of kilts, blouses instead of shirts. To Robin's generation, fashion was a negative thing. You didn't try to look pretty, or smart. You just tried not to look like a creep.

Susan followed her daughter into the kitchen, where Robin was pouring herself a glass of milk and picking over the cookie jar, avoiding the chocolate ones that might cause pimples.

"Is Daddy coming home tonight?" she asked.

"Yes, he said he'd be on the five-oh-eight, if he didn't telephone by three."

"And he didn't?"

"No. I'll be going to the station in a few minutes."

"He's spending a lot of time in town."

"He's been working on that play he wrote long ago before we were married. It's easier for him to work in the office than out here."

"Why?"

"There aren't so many interruptions. The office is empty after five."

"What did the doctor say about Buzz?"

"In six months, he should be walking without braces. By the time he's twenty, no one will ever know he had polio."

Robin rinsed her milky glass at the sink. "We were lucky, weren't we?"

"We're always lucky, didn't you know?"

"I don't believe Buzz realizes how lucky he was. He's getting awfully cranky."

"Wouldn't you be cranky if you'd spent a whole year in bed?"

"Maybe, but he ought to understand how hard it's been on you and Dad, especially you." Robin's side-glance was startlingly like her father's, charged with things she left unsaid underlining the things she did say. "Do you know you spend far more time with Buzz than you do with Dad or me?"

"Do I?"

"You ought to let me take care of Buzz after school, now and then. That way, you could have dinner with Daddy in New York, the way you used to, and come home together on a late train."

"I doubt if Daddy would want to take me out to dinner while he's working so hard on the play. The evening is the only time he has to work on it. . . . Heavens, I must run! His train is due in two minutes."

Susan was hardly conscious of driving the familiar road to the station. The old car, like an old horse, found its own way into the parking lot and turned itself around, so it would be headed out, after the train came in. Susan lit a cigarette. Only then did she notice that Janet Morley was in the car beside her.

"Hello, Susan! I'm pooped. Spent the whole day with poor Kate Trumbull. Know her?"

"I've met her a few times. I don't know her well."

"I forgot. You're not a joiner. She was. Women's Club, PTA, League of Women Voters, and all that jazz."

"But not now?"

"Her husband divorced her a year ago. They'd been married twenty-one years and the children were all in college. It was one of those sudden things, a shock to Janet, who had no idea it was coming. She blew her top completely. Spent eight months in Crossways Sanitarium. She's home now, with a practical nurse."

"I suppose the nurse helps with the housework?"

"Hell, no! The nurse is there only to see that Kate does the housework herself. Occupational therapy. Her psychiatrist was afraid she'd slop around all day in an old dressing-gown and eat nothing but crackers and milk."

Susan felt as if she were hearing about a life as remote from her own as life in China or Peru. "You mean Kate pays the nurse to order her around in her own house and cooks for the nurse as well?"

"It's good for her. She has to adjust."

"To what?"

"To life."

"But what life has she got now? She's lost everything. Husband gone, children grown. Why shouldn't she slop around in an old gown and eat crackers and milk, if she wants to?"

"It's plain to be seen you've never been a trained social worker," said Janet, who had been just that before her marriage. "Kate must become a useful member of society again."

"What became of the husband?"

"The usual. He married his secretary. Twenty years younger than Kate."

Janet stopped speaking as she saw the headlight of the engine through the dusk. The train ground to an apparently reluctant halt and men with brief-cases began pouring out of cars. The women who didn't see their men looked anxious, but not Susan. Bob was always the last off the train, strolling across the platform, alone.

And so he was tonight. But not alone.

The girl, who walked beside him, was almost as tall as he and she looked youngish — somewhere in her early thirties. Susan's feminine eye took in a long, loose, shabby coat, shaped like a tent, a touselled, Italian haircut, shoes with tall heels

and sharply pointed toes. The face was chubby and, with a
flash of relief, Susan noted that it had no claim to prettiness
at all.

"Hi, darling!" Bob bent to kiss her. "This is Kyra Novacz,
who's been typing my play for me. I should have called you
about her, but there just wasn't time. Her father took off for
Washington suddenly, and she was so damned lonely, I said:
'Come along and spend a week-end in the country with us.'
So she did."

"I should have made him call you, Mrs. Lundy." Kyra's
voice was smaller than ever and bland as butter. "I know this
must seem like an imposition, but . . ."

Bob put his arm around Susan. "I told Kyra I didn't have
that kind of wife. The kind that makes a fuss when an un-
expected guest arrives."

"Of course you don't." Susan was able to put a sincerity
into her voice that she might not have achieved if Kyra had
been pretty. "Bob has told me a lot about you and we're both
so grateful to you for helping him with his play."

"I love typing something interesting like that," said Kyra.
"It's such a change from the dry, old minutes of U.N. com-
mittee meetings."

"I'm sorry your father couldn't come, too. Perhaps some
other time . . . ?"

"I'm sure he'd love it out here." Kyra's glance flicked the
snowy fields around the station. "It's awfully sweet of you to
think of Dada."

Bob tossed Kyra's suitcase into the back seat and slid into
the driver's seat, pushing it back to accommodate his legs, so
much longer than Sue's. Sue and Kyra sat beside him, Kyra
next to Bob because Sue, with reflex politeness, had waited
for Kyra to get in first.

A small, foreign car shot across their bows at high speed.

"Dashing home for that first Martini!" said Bob. "We'll take our time and get there all in one piece." He leaned across Kyra to squeeze one of Susan's knees between thumb and forefinger — a little caress she had known for many years.

She studied his face as they drove down the winding road and, for a few moments, forgot all about Kyra. Bob was looking tired, almost ill. Not his usual, buoyant self at all. Commuting was hard on a man over fifty. Maybe they should take an apartment in New York, maybe he should retire. . . .

Kyra's voice cut across her thoughts. "Shall we tell Susan our wonderful news, Bob?"

"Oh, yes." Bob turned sidewise in his seat, only one hand on the wheel. "Lou Symington is interested in the play. She's going to read it this week-end."

"That's marvelous!" cried Susan.

"It was Kyra's idea, showing the script to Lou. This gal has a brain. She took the script right over to Lou, when she finished typing it."

"I didn't even know Lou was still in New York," said Susan.

"She's on location here shooting — what's the name of that thing?"

"*Still Waters,*" said Kyra promptly and Sue had a sudden feeling of awkwardness, as if she were the country cousin, who didn't know what was going on in the great world, where Bob and Kyra spent most of their time.

Kyra turned her head to look at Sue. "Most wives would be scared to death to have a husband working with a woman like Lou Symington."

Sue smiled. "I'll take a chance on Lou, or any of those Hollywood goddesses, where Bob is concerned. He's the one who creates their public images and, you know, an image-maker does not believe in the gods ... or the goddesses. If ever Bob went off the rails, it would be with someone quite different, probably someone quite plain and dull."

"Don't worry, Mrs. Lundy," said Kyra. "Bob will never go off the rails. He cares too much for you."

"Nobody calls me Mrs. Lundy these days," said Sue. "In another generation, I'm sure surnames will become extinct. You'd better start calling me Susan now."

"And I'm Kyra." She smiled and her little eyes vanished behind her chubby cheeks. "Is this your house?" she exclaimed, as they turned into the driveway. "How perfectly lovely! Everything that a Westchester house should be."

Sue had a funny feeling that Kyra, like German occupation troops, was determined that her behavior should be "korrekt" in every detail. This remark was a part of that correctness.

As Bob opened the front door, Buzz limped towards him. Bob dropped Kyra's suitcase and took the boy in his arms. "How's my son?"

Two years ago Buzz had been sturdy, handsome, high-spirited. Now he was pale and wizened and his eyes looked old.

"Bored. There's nothing to do here."

"We've got a guest, Buzz. Miss Novacz."

"Hello, Miss Novacz," Buzz looked at her dully.

"I've heard a lot about you," said Kyra. "I have a box of candy for you in my suitcase."

More correctness, thought Sue. There will be a small bottle of perfume for me and a big bottle of *eau de Cologne* for Robin.

"Chocolate?" demanded Buzz.

"Wait a minute." Bob looked at Sue reprovingly. "Doesn't your mother ever tell you to say 'thank you?' "

"Only about fifty times a day." Buzz looked up at Kyra

with a disarmingly impish smile. "Thank you," he said gravely.

"I'll show you to your room," Sue drew Kyra towards the stair. Bob was looking at Buzz in a puzzled way. Sue thought: now he's the outsider. He's seen so little of Buzz the last few months, he's forgotten how to talk to the boy.

"Haven't you any books to read?" Bob asked Buzz.

"No. I finished *Green Mansions*. No other book could be as good as that, so I'm not going to read any more."

"Homework?"

"It's all done."

"TV?"

"That's for little kids. There's nothing for me to do now. I wish I was dead."

"Oh, come on, Buzz!" Bob managed a laugh. "Think how lucky you are! You might have been in an iron lung."

"Oh, great! I'm lucky because I'm not in an iron lung. I wanted Robin to play cards with me this afternoon, but she wouldn't. Said she had to do her own homework."

"Would you like me to play cards with you?"

"Oh, Dad, would you?" Buzz's face glowed.

"Sure. I'll teach you to play poker, if Mommy doesn't catch me."

Susan caught them, a few minutes later, on either side of a table loaded with cards and chips. They were so absorbed, they didn't hear her come into the living room.

"I'll raise you." Bob pushed forward a stack of red chips.

Buzz looked at the poker chips with satisfaction as if he were realizing a dream of many years' standing. When he spoke, his voice was hushed, with a touch of awe for the experience he was having:

"Now all we need are drinks and guns!"

He didn't understand his father's laughter. His mother

laughed, too, but it was a wry laugh. The childish innocence revealed by the remark had such a fleeting quality. In only a few more years, Buzz would know that life was not like the stylized scenes he saw on TV.

"I can't do anything about guns," said Sue. "But I'll get drinks right away. Martinis for us and a Coke for Buzz."

She turned and discovered Kyra, watching the scene from the doorway. Kyra's glance moved slowly about the living-room, taking in every detail — the smiling faces of mother, father and son, the Christmas wreaths sparkling in the fire-light, the drawn curtains that shut out the desolate winter night beyond all this warmth and security. When she spoke, her voice, like Buzzy's a moment ago, was hushed, with a touch of awe.

"This is a happy home. You feel it the moment you cross the threshold."

Sue found herself warming to the girl. "Some day you'll have a home of your own just as happy."

Kyra looked at Sue without smiling. "I hope so. I'd do anything to get it. Anything."

"Maybe I can help," said Sue. "There are a lot of nice young men in this neighborhood."

When Bob and Sue were alone in their own room that night, Sue said: "Tell me more about this girl, Kyra what's her name."

"Novacz. Spelled N O V A C Z."

Bob was already in bed. Sue was brushing her hair at the dressing table. He lit a cigarette and went on: "Kyra's been a real help with the play. Not just the typing, but getting Lou Symington interested."

"Where did you first meet Kyra?"

Bob told her.

"And you've never met the father?"

"He's always been out when I went to her apartment. I've only been there twice. She's been coming up to the office around five with stuff she typed during the day and then we'd go over it together for typos. I've taken her out to dinner a few times, because she won't let me pay her for the typing and I've got to do something for her. I was awfully glad she was able to come out here. I knew you and she would like each other."

Sue sighed. There were times when she wished Bob wouldn't take quite so many lame ducks under his wing. They were always ducks. A lame drake would have been a nice change.

She spoke slowly. "You really don't know anything about her, do you?"

"I don't have to know anything about her. The moment I laid eyes on her, I could see she was a nice girl. Funny thing is, I have an odd feeling I've seen her somewhere before."

Sue put down her hairbrush and slid between the sheets. Bob put out his cigarette and switched off the bedside lamp. For a few moments he held her in his arms. Then, when the position became uncomfortable for both of them, he rolled over on his other side with his back towards her, but one arm stretched behind his back and his hand clasped hers for a moment, wordlessly. It was his way of saying: I'm turning my back, but not because I don't love you! Just because I'm tired and want to be comfortable and go to sleep. . . .

She closed her eyes, feeling cherished, secure and peaceful. In a few moments, she was asleep.

Bob closed his eyes, but sleep did not come right away. He was in that drowsy state when memory slides easily from conscious recollection to the vivid hallucination of dreams. One moment, he was just thinking of Kyra. The next moment, he was seeing her in bright color, sitting across the table from him at Burano's restaurant, where they had dined the evening she finished typing the play, and then, suddenly, he was awake again.

He lit another cigarette, moving quietly so as not to wake Sue. He was sorry in a way that the play was finished. What would he do with his evenings now? How pleasant it had been, at the end of each day's work, to have Kyra surge suddenly into his office, all eagerness and youth, with twenty or thirty more pages of the typed script. He would pour drinks in paper cups from the bottle in his desk and they would go over the script together, pointing out especially good lines of dialogue to each other. She always liked the same lines he did — that was really quite a coincidence. But she was intelligent, not like the vacuous slick-chicks in the stenographic pool who read comic books during the lunch hour.

And then those occasional dinners with Kyra at Burano's had added the spice of conspiracy to his life. He had lied to Sue about them, told her he was working late and grabbing a sandwich, and Kyra had lied to her father in the same way, each pretending he or she was dining alone. There was a curiously pleasant sense of mischief in keeping a little thing like that a secret, innocent as the secret was. It made a man feel young to do something mischievous, something playful. Age was always pompous.

Now he was wide awake and restless. Still moving stealthily, he slid out of bed, careful not to disarrange the bed clothes around Sue. Maybe a nightcap would make him sleepy once more.

He didn't grope for dressing-gown and slippers. That might have wakened Sue. In pajamas and bare feet, he tip-toed to the door and shut it softly behind him.

In the living-room, moonlight was pouring through the French window that led to the terrace, so brightly he did not stop to switch on a light. Half-way across the room, he stopped as if he had been shot.

There on the sofa, lay Kyra, bathed in the fairy light of the full moon and naked — a statue carved in mother-of-pearl.

She was lying on her back, her hands clasped behind her head, so that the tightened pectoral muscles lifted her breasts against the pull of gravity. She didn't speak. She turned her head and smiled, her little teeth like pearls in the moonlight.

"Are you crazy?" he whispered.

"Perhaps. It's warm in this house. I like an air bath and I couldn't resist the moon." Her voice dropped, "Can you?"

He moved like a hypnotized subject in preconditioned response to a signal from the hypnotist. His fingertips touched one of her breasts. His mouth wandered over her hair and came to rest upon her mouth.

She turned her cheek away from him. "Do you realize we have no excuse for meeting any more? The play is finished."

He nodded.

"What are we going to do?"

Before he could answer, her lips were on his, clinging and sucking, drawing all his strength out of him. Her head fell back at last. She thrust herself away from him with an impetus that moved the old sofa on its creaking castors. Her eyes were brilliant in her flushed face as she whispered: "I love you. I love you so much I want the whole world to know I love you. I love you so much I want to bear your child."

"Kyra!" he cried out. "I want you. I need you. I love you. God, how I love you!"

The sudden blaze of light startled both of them. Even before he turned his head, Bob knew he would see Susan standing in the doorway.

CHAPTER FIVE

HAPPINESS, LIKE LIFE itself, takes years to nurture, but can be destroyed forever in a few seconds. Only realization takes time. A mortal wound is too great a shock to be painful immediately. To Susan, time seemed to slow and grind to a stop. Everything froze, like a moving picture when the projector jams.

She could not look at Kyra. The sight of the woman hurt her eyes with a physical ache, like a blinding light. That was one reason she turned and went back into her own room. She could not look at Kyra, let alone speak to her. Not at this moment.

It was only many months later that Susan wondered if it might not have been better for everyone concerned if she had been the sort of woman who screams and slaps faces and pulls hair. At least, the others would have known then how she felt. This way, they could have no idea. The French crowds, seeing the aristocrats go to the guillotine with stony faces, watched them as stonily. But when DuBarry, the streetwalker, screamed her fear, the crowd rioted in her favor and came near to saving her.

Only when Susan was alone did time stir reluctantly and move on. And, with the return of time-sense, came realization. Life had not ended, only happiness. What was she going to do now? What would happen to Buzz and Robin, Bob and herself?

She never knew how long she sat there, alone. At last, the door opened and Bob came into the room. He came straight towards her. "Oh, God, Sue!" He knelt and buried his face in her lap. Her arms cradled his head and, for a moment, she thought that nothing had happened, that nothing was lost.

He sat back on his heels and lifted a tragic face to hers, a face twisted as if he were in physical pain. Her heart went out to him, yet she held her peace. She could not think of anything to say.

Then he spoke. "There will be no divorce unless you insist upon it."

"Divorce?" It was a word in a foreign language. "Why should I want a divorce?"

"Because I'm in love with Kyra and I cannot give her up."

She had thought she knew pain a moment ago, but it was nothing to this. It is one thing to have a knife plunged into your heart, quite another thing to have it twisted.

"You ... love ... her?"

"Yes."

"Why?"

"I don't know. Perhaps because she loves me."

"Are you quite sure of that?"

"Quite sure."

"And the fact that I love you no longer matters?"

"Of course it matters, Darling Sue, I love you. I always shall."

"But you can't love two women at once!"

"Why not? Perhaps men can. I think I do. What is love?"

"How can you love a girl like that?"

"Like what? You'll have to admit that she's a nice girl."

"A nice girl!" Anger can be as healing as tears, the release of emotions too violent to hold in check for any length of time without psychological damage, but, unfortunately, the effect of anger on others is too high a price to pay for that release. After a few minutes the hot, bitter words died on Susan's lips. She was doing two extremely stupid things. She was using rational argument to a man in love, which is as fatuous as reasoning with a drunken man, and, in criticizing Kyra she was criticizing Bob's taste in women, something no man can endure. Years ago, she remembered a cynical friend telling her: "You can sometimes criticize a man's wife and get away with it, but don't ever dare to criticize his mistress. The guilt involved in that relationship makes him pathologically sensitive to the slightest criticism of her."

"I suppose I can't expect you to like her now," said Bob in the sudden silence. "I'm sorry. In the beginning, I was so sure you and she would be friends. I thought you could be such a help to her."

Susan spoke quietly. "Bob, how can you love a girl who is doing what she is doing? She is threatening Robin's happiness and Buzzy's. The only sexual act that is really immoral is one that hurts a child."

"But she's doing it for me," said Bob. "Because she loves me so much."

"I see." Sue fought for self-control. "I think of her as immoral, and you think of her as a moral person who has done an immoral thing, only because her love for you is so great. And the more I accuse her of doing a wickedly immoral thing, the more I build up in your mind your concept of the vast extent of her love for you."

"But she is a moral person, Sue. She's a nice person."

"I wonder if there is any such thing as a nice person? We call people nice when they're nice to us and we call them nasty when they're nasty to us. You call her nice, because you think she's been nice to you. That doesn't mean she's a nice person."

"Sue, she didn't want this to happen."

"How do you know?"

"She said so."

"How long has it been going on?"

"Three months."

"Why did you bring her out here this week-end?"

"I thought, if she saw you and the children, she would realize how impossible the whole thing was. I thought if I saw you and her together, I would realize how impossible the whole thing was. I hoped that it would end, so then we could both be friends with her. She needs friends, and things can happen that way, but . . ."

"They didn't."

"No, they didn't. I was in deeper than I knew. Oh, Sue, I can't explain it. There are times when I don't even like her, I almost hate her, but, when she wants me, I have to go to her. I've reached a point where I'm making excuses to see her whenever I can. I mustn't pull any punches. I want to live with her. I don't want to live with you."

"And the children?"

"I was wondering. . . . Could I take an apartment in town and come out for week-ends? I could put it all on work. The

play, Lou Symington, anything. Then the children wouldn't
be bothered."

"And if she got pregnant? She said she wanted to bear your
child. I heard her."

"She might . . . wait a while."

"I doubt if she would."

"It's been done," said Bob. "When the wife was strong
enough. The French do it all the time. If only we could wait
a few months before doing anything final. Maybe I'll fall out
of love with her. Maybe she'll die . . ."

It was an odd thing for a lover to say of his love. Sue realized that, for the first time in her life, she had lost all ability
to understand Bob. She wondered if he even understood himself.

She sat silent, trying to visualize what life would be like for
her and the children, if she agreed to his plan. The five-day
week without Bob, school and meals and household chores,
and lonely evenings. Then the week-ends, when she and he
would put on an act together, pretending to the children that
they still loved each other. Only I wouldn't be pretending, she
thought. I do love Bob and I always shall. How can I not love
the father of Robin and Buzzy?

"We had so much," said Bob. "We've been through so
much together. I haven't stopped loving you. But I'm in love
with her. Those two things are different."

"I must have time," Susan put her fingertips to her temples.
"I just don't know if I'm strong enough to share my husband
with another woman. I'm not sure it would be strength to do
so. It might just be callousness. Perhaps Frenchwomen are
able to do it because they don't marry for love. It's all arranged
by their families. Wives who do it can't love their husbands
the way I love you."

A harsh, inner voice was nagging her: The really strong thing to do is to gamble now and say: *You must either give her up or give up the children and me. I'll give you a month to think it over* . . . But a softer interior voice whispered: *You wouldn't be gambling with your own happiness alone. You'd be gambling with the children's happiness as well. Have you the nerve to let their whole future hang on the turn of one card? He's giving you a chance to avoid divorce for the time being. Perhaps if you can avoid it for a while you can avoid it forever and the children will never be hurt. So much can happen in a month, or a week, or even a few minutes. . . .*

"How much time do you want?" asked Bob.

"A week."

"All right. I'll pack a bag now and drive Kyra into town. She and I can't stay here after this. You'll have your week to think alone and I'll come out to talk things over next Saturday morning."

He was pulling a suitcase out of the closet.

"What shall I tell Robin and Buzz tomorrow morning?"

"Business. Some big shot arriving in New York from the Coast on a Saturday morning plane. It has happened."

She sat numb as he threw shirts and underclothes into the bag, remembering all the trips they had taken together, including their honeymoon. She watched all the little motions she knew so well — the turn of the head, the squaring of the shoulders, the set of the jaw line. She had a sense of possessiveness about this body she knew so well. He's mine, not hers. How dare she steal him?

At the same time she had a feeling of tragic compassion for Bob. He seemed to be driven by fate, not following a path he would have chosen, if man had complete free-will.

The intimate, domestic act of packing a bag, in Sue's presence, to go off with Kyra, dramatized the abstract agony in

concrete symbols, as charged emotionally as the symbolic
language of art. This wasn't just talk. This was action. Tonight
Bob would lie with Kyra, not with Sue. The details made
everything so real. She began to feel as if she were imprisoned
in a house where a fire had got out of control and human
beings were suddenly helpless and doomed. This is wrong,
she thought. It ought not to happen, it wasn't meant to happen, but now it's going to happen and there is nothing I can
do to stop it . . . Or is there? But what? Dear God, what can
I do?

He closed the bag and snapped the hasps and turned to
look at her. In other, lesser crises, he had always been one to
leap before he looked and never count the consequences until
it was too late. That impulsiveness was one of his most en-
dearing traits, one of the things that had kept him youthful,
but now it was plunging all of them into an abyss.

She rose and moved towards him. "Oh, Bob!" The long-
delayed tears came into her eyes. He took her in his arms and
again his face twisted, as if he were in physical pain. "Try to
think of it this way: it was an accident. Like driving a rickety
car, too fast, on a curving road."

They kissed with passion. It was he who broke away violently, as if he were afraid her kiss would weaken his resolu-
tion to go off with Kyra. "I don't know how we came to this
pass . . . but we did." At the door he paused, tortured and
torn between opposing forces:

"I don't suppose you want to say good-bye to Kyra?"

"No. I hate her. She has taught me the meaning of the
word hate."

"You really hate Kyra?" There was wonder in his voice and,
more, complete incomprehension. This was macabre, a complete failure of communication between them. Obviously he
did not understand how anyone could hate Kyra, because he

did not hold Kyra to blame in any way. He regarded her, like himself, as an innocent, involuntary victim of the love-goddess that the Greeks so wisely feared. He had no conception of the agony Sue felt, an agony so great that she had to hate at least one of the two lovers.

Sue's hate was stampeding her thoughts like a herd of wild cattle. She tried to hold them back. It was imperative now that she sit down and think soberly and coherently about Kyra, with as little hate as possible, for hate is blind, as well as love, and the whole future would depend to a large extent on Sue's ability to see Kyra as she really was.

Could Kyra, conceivably, be the way Bob saw her? Lonely, inexperienced, loving, caught up in an emotional storm, which she had not started and could not control? Or was she as Susan saw her — cold-hearted, calculating, ruthless from the beginning, not a woman in love with Bob, but a woman out to exploit him? And, if Susan's view was the right one, would Bob ever see the truth when the illusion was so much more flattering?

She heard the front door close, then the door of the car. She did not go to the window. She looked at the bedside clock. Four A.M. She turned out the light and lay down on the bed where Bob had lain and buried her face in his pillow. Hot tears burned her cheeks, but she made no sound. There was something unreal about the whole thing now, as if she would wake up tomorrow morning and find Bob beside her in the bed, smiling as if nothing had happened. And she would say: "Bob, I had the most horrible dream. . . ."

Finally, she rolled over on her back and lay still, letting her eyes dry. She was tired, but she could not sleep. What was that queer thing Bob had said?

Maybe she'll die . . .

CHAPTER SIX

As the car sped towards New York, Bob's surface feeling was one of relief. The weeks of uncertainty, doubt and deception were over. Everything was in the open now. Susan knew. It was like lancing a boil. The pus ran forth, the swelling collapsed, the soreness healed. He felt free.

He was aware of Kyra, stealing glances at him as if she were trying to measure his mood. He reached out a hand and pressed hers. She smiled tremulously, tears gathering in her eyes. "Oh, Bob, I didn't want to be the one to break up your marriage. This is awful. Poor Susan!"

"Nonsense!" said Bob, cheerfully. "This is the twentieth century. Thank God, we're not living in Victorian times! Did you know the divorce rate in San Francisco is fifty per cent of the marriages? In another generation, I bet it'll be a hundred per cent. Marriage just isn't for keeps any more. Every civilized person knows that."

"But Sue is so unhappy."

"She'll get over it. I've known dozens of divorced women who were perfectly happy."

"And the children?"

Bob winced. "Hey! Don't you want me to marry you? Anybody would think you were on the other side!"

Kyra realized this was no time to probe, important as probing was. "Oh, Bob . . . my Bob! I just can't put it into words." She slid across the seat to lean against him. He put an arm around her, driving with one hand. His face had the same rapt look that comes across the face of a very small child holding a very large box of very sticky candy. He could not see Kyra's face; his eyes were on the road, her cheek against his shoulder. Her eyes were half-closed, thoughtful.

"I want you to be sure — very sure," whispered Kyra. "I wouldn't want you, if you were not sure."

"I'm sure." His arm squeezed her shoulder.

At the first toll station, he came out of trance. "Sue has asked for a week to think things out. I don't want you to go back to your father now. I want you with me. Let's take a suite in a New York hotel together."

"Dada wouldn't like that."

"Does that matter?"

"Not to me now. . . . What do you think Susan will do, Bob?"

He frowned at that one. "I don't know. If she's realistic, she'll decide on divorce right away. If she tries for the other thing — you and me living together in New York and my going out to Westchester often enough to fool the children, I don't think it will work. I think it will be too great a strain on her. She'll try not to care, but she does care and she'll make angry scenes. That'll be worse for the children than divorce.

In a few months, she'll have to give up. She'll have to admit that she and I can't live together unless I give you up. And I won't give you up. I made that clear to her."

"Oh, my darling . . ."

He squeezed her shoulder again. "At the latest, you'll be my wife in six months."

Kyra smiled and stretched luxuriously as a cat before a warm hearth. "My Bob! What a wonderful life we'll have together. Just the two of us. Unless God is good to me, and I can give you a child."

Bob smiled. "It's like starting life all over again. Do you know, Kyra, you've made me feel as if I were eighteen? What man of fifty wouldn't do anything for that?"

"Anything?" breathed Kyra.

"Well, anything short of murder."

"Some men have even murdered . . . for love."

"That's something I could never understand. I'd run away to South America with you, if I had to, but I wouldn't kill anybody who stood in our way. That's nuts."

"Not even if it were the only way we could be together?"

"But it isn't, so the whole thing is academic. And I don't believe murderers kill for love alone. They kill because they want love and something else — usually money or respectability. I don't care for either one, but, even if I did, I wouldn't take a human life. There's only one justification for killing, self-defense. Of course that includes the defense of someone you love whose life is in immediate, physical danger."

"I would kill for you," whispered Kyra.

"Child, you don't know what you're saying." Bob looked at her, deeply moved. What a sweet kid she was, and with what terrifyingly whole-hearted innocence she loved him. She, who had probably never seen death, talking of killing for his sake ... She asked nothing for herself. She had no assurance that Sue would give him a divorce, and no assurance that he would be able to support her, as well as Sue and the children, whom he was bound to care for. Yet, her love was so selfless, that she was ready to cast her father, her future, everything to the winds for his sake. It was a debt he could never repay her, even if he devoted all the rest of his life to making her happy.

Kyra stirred within his arm. "Dawn ..."

They could see the Hudson now as they approached the last toll booth before the West Side Highway. The road curved and rose sharply. For a moment they could see nothing beyond the rim of the rise but water and the Jersey palisades faintly flushed with a pink reflection of the red sky behind them.

Bob felt a surge of that emotion, almost mystical, which sometimes flowers from the earthy roots of sex. The air was so sweet, so still, so windless, the dawn light, so pure, so innocent, so young. The world was newly made, just dropped from the hand of God in shining perfection. This was the Garden of Eden. He was Adam, she was Eve, and the whole of human life lay before them, not behind them. It was glorious to be alive and in love.

His mood shattered when another car sped past them a little too close for comfort and brought him back to the real world of traffic laws and other people who were not happy. But he felt that the moment would shine like a star in his memory long after everything else there had darkened.

They left the car at the parking lot on the site of the old Hippodrome Theatre and wandered about the empty, sunlit streets hand in hand, looking for an all-night automat and failing to find one. Finally they came back to the Algonquin, opposite the parking lot, for breakfast.

Love is one of the several diseases that number euphoria among their symptoms. Bob was in that state where all food is ambrosia and all waiters deserve a double tip.

"We'll find a smaller hotel," he said, over his second cup of coffee. "Too many reporters around here."

Kyra slid her arm through his as they strolled towards Fifth Avenue. "Oh, what fun it is to walk around the city with an attractive man who loves you!" Her voice carolled, matching her smile. "Everything looks different, brighter, gayer. Do you see how all the women look at me with envy? I hope they all find men as nice as you. Today I'm so happy I love everybody. Today I wish everybody could be as happy as I. It's winter, but spring is bubbling and singing inside me. Oh, Bob, this is what life was made for."

He looked down at her fondly, in both meanings of the word — affectionate and foolish. Perhaps all affection is folly, and our language tacitly acknowledges this.

"It hurts, doesn't it?" he whispered.

"What does?"

"Love, beauty, happiness . . ."

His gaze took in the whole scene. It was one of those bright, wintry days when Manhattan is at its best, an imperial city. The square, sharp edges of the buildings cut the brilliant blue of the sky into geometric shapes. The snowfall, lighter here than in the country, lingered only in the gutters, washing the pavements clean. The Christmas trees were up on Park Avenue and great, gaudy, tinsel wreaths glittered in all the shop windows.

It was Kyra who realized that they were passing Bob's office. "Do you know it's after nine? Oughtn't you to stop in for a moment?"

"It's Saturday. But there may be some messages. I suppose

I ought to tell them I'll be in town all this week-end."

Kyra was already a familiar figure in Bob's office. They had worked on the play after hours, but some of the staff was usually still around when Kyra arrived.

"Hello, Miss Novacz!" The receptionist's smile said plainly that she knew what was going on. Her glow flattered both of them by reflecting their own radiance, and gave Kyra's step an added buoyancy, as she walked down the corridor beside Bob.

He stood before his desk, overcoat open, hat pushed to the back of his head, glancing through letters and messages that had come in yesterday afternoon. Something bold and piratical in his stance suggested one of those movie reporters, who strolls into his office at noon, answers back to his boss, makes one phone call and then shouts: "Stop the presses!"

"Ah, ha! A call from Lou Symington, kid. Hold on to your *béret!* Here we go!"

"Oh . . ." Kyra gasped. "I'm praying . . ."

"Outside line, please . . ." Bob dropped one hip on a corner of the desk and began to dial. "Miss Symington, please . . . Yes, she's expecting the call . . . Yes, I'll wait . . . Lou? Bob Lundy here. Just got your message to call you . . ."

Kyra held her breath.

Sex was a powerful thing, but other things helped it along. Offering the play to Lou Symington had been her idea. If it ended in rebuff and humiliation for Bob, it could hardly help tarnishing the brightness of their relationship a little. Ancient Persian kings may be the only people who killed messengers bringing bad news, but everyone would like to.

"That's great, Lou. That's the kind of thing an author likes to hear. And coming from you . . ."

Kyra let her breath go.

God was on her side. She couldn't fail now. And, if the play were a hit, there would be money enough for Sue and the children to make Bob feel less guilty. For there was guilt, deep down, under all that bravado, and Kyra was afraid of that guilt. In time, it might do strange things to Bob, and to her.

"Sure, I'll be right over . . . Kyra's here with me now, I'll bring her along . . ." He put down the phone. "Well, this calls for a celebration!"

Hat still on the back of his head, overcoat swinging jauntily as a cavalier's cloak, he opened the desk drawer where he kept a bottle and paper cups.

But, before he could pour a drink, Kyra slid into his arms as smoothly as an eel slides into the mud. "Darling Bob, I'm so happy for you!" She locked her arms around his neck and sealed his lips with hers and held them there, warm and soft as melting wax. Since the gamble with the play had succeeded everything must be done now to make him associate it with her, not just with drinks and celebrations.

They gave themselves up to caresses and broken whispers until a girl from the stenographers' pool opened the door, blushed under rouge, and backed out with a hasty: "Par'me!"

Bob broke away. "We'd better get over to the Waldorf. I told Lou right away."

Kyra smiled, cheeks flushed, eyes sparkling. "I don't care if that girl did see us!"

"Well, we haven't exactly made this thing a secret in the last twenty-four hours!" Bob's humor was seasoned with a touch of rue that troubled Kyra, but her smile was indefatigable.

Arm in arm, they swept through the outer office, still with that ruthless disregard for appearances that marks the early stages of love. They were happy and nothing else mattered. They were the only people in the world made of flesh and

blood. The others were paper dolls who couldn't feel or weep
or bleed.

Lou Symington received them *en negligée* — a *bouffante*
cloud of white lace, girdled with rose-colored ribbons that
matched her little shoes and made her look like a dark, Spanish bride. She kissed Kyra. She kissed Bob. Dick said: "Hi,"
and "What'll it be?" and the inevitable drinking began.

Lou lay back on a sofa, and a graceful drift of lace fell away
from her feet toward the floor, thinning her skirt. The outline
of her heavily insured legs could be seen clearly through the
lace. Bob stared, Lou smiled, and Kyra's eyes narrowed. Already she felt the sharp prick of that first tax on possession,
jealousy. She realized how slender her hold was on Bob and
she prayed, silently, that Susan would be too stupid to realize
this. Bob called it love, but Kyra herself knew that her only
real hold on him as yet was sex. True, it was romantic sex, all
dressed up in pink, sugared almonds and perfumed lace-paper,
but, underneath these frills, it was still just sex and Susan had
so much more on her side — love, memories, children . . .

Kyra moved her chair until it was between Bob and his view
of Lou Symington's legs.

"The third act is terrific," said Dick Grant. "A perfect ve-
hicle for Lou. The only question is whether or not to do it as
a play on Broadway and then as a movie, or just as a movie."

"I've always wanted a crack at Broadway," said Lou.

"Who doesn't?" retorted Dick. "Trouble is, most movie
actresses come an awful cropper there. No camera angles, and
all those lines to learn, all at once, not just one scene at a time.
Tough, baby."

"I know I could!"

"Oh, you could, and we could raise the hundred grand, or
so, to back the show and be co-producers, so our profits would
be almost tax-free, just capital net gains. But suppose there

are no profits? Your box office hasn't been so good lately."

"That's just that damn divorce business."

"Okay, but a flop on Broadway would make it worse, whatever the cause. Your only hope now is to come up with a string of sure-fire hits so God damned good that all these prudes and puritans will have to keep their big mouths shut. You've got to smother them in your beauty and talent. If you falter for a moment, if you're in one bad flop, the pack of wolves will be on your back and tear you limb from limb. But, if you're a success, and millions are invested in your success, we can hire a dozen firms like K., K., D., and V., to brainwash the rubes and we'll be sitting pretty. That's why I say do a movie and the hell with Broadway."

Lou pouted and grumbled and finally gave in. At heart, she was always practical. Dick Grant began to talk money and Bob tried to conceal his unfamiliarity with the enormous sums Dick mentioned so airily. He kept his head enough to demand a tiny percentage of the gross profits instead of a decent percentage of the net, knowing only too well, that there would be no net by the time Dick's accountants got through with the gross receipts. The net was a myth, like the unicorn, an illusion kept alive only so playwrights could be dazzled by the offer of a handsome percentage of nothing.

Finding Bob this knowledgeable, Dick said: "How about taking a piece of the show yourself and being co-producer? Think what that would do for you tax-wise. Good, old, capital net gain!"

"It would have to be a rather small piece," said Bob.

"Sure, just a token, chickenfeed. Say forty or fifty thousand. I wouldn't dream of sticking you."

"I'll think about it." Bob rose. "We'd better be getting along, Kyra."

Dick followed them to the door. "I'll send this rough draft

of the contract over to my lawyers and they'll put it in shape
and then we can sign it. Let me know by Monday if you do
want a piece of the show. You've got a hit on your hands, boy.
You're going places."

"Glad you think so."

"As a movie, it should put Lou back on her feet again."
His hard eyes shifted to Kyra for a moment, then came back
to Bob. "It's nice that you're a steady, family man with a wife
and two kids in Westchester. That's good public relations. It
will offset Lou's peccadilloes and make the hicks forget that
she and I are a couple of tramps. So long!"

The door closed. The thick carpet silenced their steps as
they walked towards the elevator.

Bob was angry. "What the hell did Dick mean by that last
crack? What business is it of his that you and I . . . Dick
Grant, of all people! The werewolf of the San Fernando valley!"

Kyra was shrewd enough to see one reason Dick's remark
annoyed Bob so much. To the twentieth century male, divorce is, among other things, a luxury. Having only one wife
was like having only one car. But having several wives proved
that you were important enough to ignore a large section of
public opinion and prosperous enough to support more than
one family. No man would think of it consciously in such
crude terms, but there was a generalized, unconscious feeling
that an important man was usually a divorced man. If Bob had
expected any reaction from Dick at all, Bob had, no doubt,
expected to be welcomed by Dick into the polygamous society
of the elect, not to be curtly warned off, as if he were not one
of the elect after all.

Kyra's pale, brittle voice always lent a tone of timidity to her
words. "Bob," she fluted, almost fearfully. "Isn't there usually

a morals clause in a movie contract?"

"So what?" The hard, reckless anger in Bob's eyes would have frightened some women. "Scandal is all they mind. There'll be no scandal about us. Mexican divorce. Quiet wedding."

"But once you're a successful playwright, you'll be a celebrity and —"

"Oh, be quiet!" He stabbed the elevator button with his thumb.

He had never spoken to her in that tone before, but she was wise enough to hold her tongue. She knew his anger was not for her. It came out of that buried guilt she feared so much. Perhaps he was beginning to realize what she had realized several minutes ago. If he were not now planning to support two households he and Sue together might have managed to raise a few thousands to invest in his play — a loan from a bank or something like that. So it just might be that Bob had lost a fortune as well as a home because of Kyra.

She knew Bob well enough by this time to know that money alone did not sway his decisions. But, if he did lose the chance to make a great deal of money because of her, the fact would always be there, in his unconscious mind, in years to come, and it would feed his sense of guilt, especially if Sue or the children ever suffered from a real lack of money in the future.

The elevator dropped swiftly, tugging at their entrails with an almost erotic sensation. A moment ago, Kyra had been thinking of the weaknesses of her position. Now she suddenly saw one of its great strengths — shared guilt. The more they became outcasts, the tighter the bond between them would be, by a sort of cantilever process simply because they were fellow-outcasts. It was they against the world. They had got each other into this and now neither one could, in honor, let the other down. So Bob was compelled to resent fiercely any jibe based on his relation with Kyra, like this unfortunate remark of Dick Grant's. He was now committed to Kyra, more irrevocably than he would be if they were married. Loyalty to a wife is like paying a tradesman's bill. You can be sued, if you don't. But loyalty to a mistress is like a gambling debt, a debt of dishonor. Just because Kyra had no legal power to enforce any claim on him, her claim was one he had to acknowledge before all others, or lose his self-respect.

Ironically enough, the most important step in their relation had been made not by Kyra herself, but by Susan when she found Bob and Kyra together. Once that happened, Bob had to convince himself, as well as Susan, that he loved Kyra. Once that happened, it became almost psychologically impossible for Bob ever to say to Susan: "I've changed my mind. I was mistaken. I don't love her after all. I want to come back to you." It would make Bob weak in his own eyes to have caused Susan so much pain for anything less than a great love. Now he would have to make Kyra the great love of his life in self-justification.

Kyra felt a great wave of elation. He was hooked. She had caught him. He couldn't get away from her, no matter what happened . . . And he didn't want to get away from her. She was sure of that now and the sureness gave her a new sense of power.

"We'd better not register at a hotel as Mr. and Mrs. Robert Lundy," said Bob as they walked down Park Avenue. "There's no point in leaving evidence like that lying around." Apparently Dick Grant had revived his sense of caution. "There's a little hotel on Park Avenue South, where K., K., D., and V. put up clients from Hollywood who are not as important as Lou Symington. I've often sent starlets there. You just go in and register as Kyra Novacz. Then I'll come in and register as Robert Lundy. Ask for a suite on the fourteenth floor, and I'll get a place on the fourteenth floor too."

"But wouldn't even that be evidence of ... ?"

"It's evidence of nothing that would stand up in court."

"I don't know if I have enough money for a suite."

"I owe you about a hundred and fifty bucks for typing the play. That should cover it."

Kyra was touched by a delicacy that assumed she had earned the money typing.

She went into the hotel lobby first. Bob was right behind her, so he could overhear the number of her suite.

But when Bob, in turn, asked for room on the fourteenth floor, the clerk said: "Sorry, sir, we just rented the last one."

"Fifteenth, then," he said, remembering the fire-stairs.

Twenty minutes later, he was in the sitting room of Kyra's suite. She had ordered ice and soda and glasses. He had brought the bottle of scotch from the office in his brief case. He tossed his jacket and necktie on the bed and sat in an arm-chair, sipping his drink. The bleating of taxi horns, the grinding of truck gears, the slither of leather soles on asphalt and a thousand other noises, less easily identified, came to them through the closed windows, orchestrated into a mutter, like the distant roar of surf.

"Off-stage noises, symbolizing New York," said Bob. "I've heard it so often on tape. Like the bird-calls that symbolize the Connecticut cottage, where the gangsters are hiding out; and the screeching parrots and monkeys that symbolize the Malayan jungle, where the bachelor engineer is making love to the Resident's wife. We never see the monkeys or birds or taxis on screen; we just hear them."

"Maybe they're not there!" Kyra laughed. "I'd better look."

She knelt on the soft carpet, resting her arms on the window-sill. She looked down, then tilted her head up, sidewise, lifting her eyes to the sky in the attitude of dreamy cherubs in old, Italian paintings. "They're there, but the whole thing looks just like a backdrop on the stage. None of it's real."

"No, none of it's real. But this." Bob kissed her and she melted into his arms. The drinks were forgotten. He fumbled with the zipper at the back of her dress . . .

By the time they were hungry again, his mood of caution had passed as swiftly as it came. "I'll be damned if I'll go down to that silly dining room. Let's have lunch up here."

"But . . ."

"I've often lunched with starlets in their suites here. No scandal at all."

He was reaching for the telephone, when Kyra laughed aloud.

"Wouldn't it look better if we had our clothes on?"

He laughed and she laughed until they found it as hard to stop laughing as it is to stop hiccuping. It had become the unmotivated laughter of love that bubbles up out of a ferment of sheer happiness.

Finally, exhausted, they dressed and finished their drinks while they were waiting for luncheon.

"I'm beginning to worry about those starlets of yours," said Kyra.

Bob looked at her. You have to tell the truth to a woman when you first fall in love with her. If she is in love with you, she'll understand. But if you lie to her at the beginning and she finds out, everything is lost.

"There were three . . . out of several dozen, over a period of ten years. They never meant a thing to me. I always went back to Susan. I always wanted to."

"Did she know?"

"I doubt it."

The waiter came and served them as if there was nothing out of the ordinary going on in this room. This time Bob was careful not to over-tip.

"I've been thinking about money," he said. "Until the play is sold, you and I should have about twelve thousand a year."

"That's more than I've ever had in my life," said Kyra.

"If the play does sell to the movies, there'll be all kinds of money for everybody."

Kyra tried to smile encouragingly and, at the same time, look as if she were indifferent to money. It was a little difficult, but Bob didn't seem to notice that.

He took his coffee over to the armchair by the window. "Now Susan knows all about us, our next job will be telling your father. Seriously, how do you think the old boy will take it?"

"Scotch in your coffee?"

"Good idea."

She poured.

Bob drank and set down his cup. "We must tell him as soon as he gets back from Washington. That's Monday morning, isn't it?"

"Yes." Kyra's eyelids dropped.

"I'll go with you. We'll tell him together . . . unless you'd rather be alone?"

"Bob!"

Something strange in her voice abraded his nerves. It was like a sudden, flat note in a piano that you had thought perfectly tuned. For a moment, he did not speak, as if he had reached a point in the story of his life where he was afraid to turn the next page, afraid of what might lie upon the other side.

You can stop reading a story, if it becomes unbearable. But

you can't stop living your own story, this side of suicide.

He turned the page. "What's the matter?"

She lifted eyes, brimming with tears.

"Kyra!"

She threw herself into his arms, sobbing. Her paroxysm lasted several minutes. He soothed her with his gentlest voice, his softest touch. Finally, she lay still, her face hidden from him, against his breast.

"Kyra." He took her face in both hands and turned it up to his. "What is it?"

"It's dreadful, horrible."

"No matter what it is, you'll have to tell me now."

"You'll be angry."

"No matter what it is, I won't be angry."

"Bob, I did it for love of you!"

"Then how could I be angry?"

"It's so messy."

"Come on, give!"

"Bob, I haven't been quite honest with you."

"In what way?"

Her lips trembled. Twice she started to speak, and gagged. Finally, the words came. "In my language, Dada is a pet name for Daniel. You thought it meant Daddy, didn't you?"

"So?"

"Bob, Dada Novacz is not my father. He's my husband."

CHAPTER SEVEN

Susan rolled over, half-awake, with a generalized sense of malaise as formless as a mist and as pervasive.
When consciousness solidified, memory returned, and her
mortal wound began to throb. There was still that odd feeling
of incredulity mixed with her sense of final catastrophe. The
mind tries hard to dissipate emotion by verbalizing it. A little
sentence formed: *Have I lost Bob?* Even then, in the beginning, when so many echoes of the explosion were as yet un-
heard, she knew this was simply another way of saying: *Have
I lost everything?*

She got out of bed, put on shirt, slacks and loafers, and ran
down to the kitchen. Orange juice, coffee, eggs, toast — the
old, familiar routine she and Bob had shared for so many
years.

Robin was the first down. "Where's Dad?"

"Asleep. Let's not make too much noise."

The first of many lies that must be told now. Truth was one
of the earliest casualties in a struggle like this. But what else
could she say, so early in the morning? That Daddy had gone

to New York in the middle of the night? She could not tell them that much truth without telling them all of it and she was not ready to do that yet. Until the decision was made to divorce or not, the less the children knew, the better for them. Perhaps they need never know...

This morning they planned to catch the nine o'clock bus at the corner which would take them down to the public library in the village. When they came back for luncheon, she could tell the second lie, the one Bob himself had suggested. He had been called into town suddenly by a visiting big shot from Hollywood and Kyra had decided to go in with him. Would two intelligent children believe all these lies?

Yes. Even if they suspected the truth, they would believe the lies, because they would so much rather believe them. If the situation went on a long time, lying would become a little game she and the children played together in order to spare each other.

Buzz brought his arithmetic book to the breakfast table. "I couldn't get this last night. If a man had a field that was twenty square acres and he ploughed nine and a half square acres in two and two thirds days.... Mom, you're not listening!"

"Sorry, Buzz."

"Two and two thirds days, how long would it take him to plough the whole field?"

Susan's mind went blank. Arithmetic had never been her favorite subject and this morning it seemed completely inaccessible.

"You ought to do your own homework," said Robin, more sternly than Susan ever spoke to Buzz.

"But I don't get it, Robin. What are you supposed to do? Multiply or divide?"

"Didn't the teacher tell you?"

"Yes, but I wasn't listening."

"Oh, Buzz!"

"Oh, Robin! I suppose you always listen to your teachers?"

"That's enough, children," Susan intervened. "Robin, leave Buzz alone. Buzz, you divide and then multiply. Now are you both ready? It's nearly nine."

"Just a minute." Buzz was dividing and Robin was waiting. Buzz wouldn't budge until he had done the problem. Robin wouldn't budge until she saw whether he got it right or not. So they both missed the bus.

"And there isn't another 'till ten!" wailed Robin. "If only this dope . . ."

"Never mind. I'll borrow Mrs. Faber's car and drive you."

"What's the matter with our car?"

"The battery's dead." Lie number three.

Jean Faber came over with the keys of her car. Susan threw a sports coat over her slacks and climbed into the driver's seat, the children beside her.

"Where's Miss Novacz?" said Buzz.

"Asleep, I guess." Susan kept her eyes on the road.

"No, she isn't. The door of her room was open and she wasn't there."

"Have you done all your arithmetic problems for Monday?" asked Susan.

"All but one. It's easy. Just percentages. I'll do that in study period Monday morning. 'Bye, Mom."

Was it, or was it not, significant that Buzz had not pursued the subject of Miss Novacz?

Susan turned the car away from the library and started to drive home. Then it came to her: home. She had no home now. Why should she hurry back to the empty house? Jean

Faber had said she didn't need the car until afternoon. The children wouldn't be back until one o'clock. That would be time enough to make beds and run the vacuum cleaner. Until then she was free. Free for what?

She drove without destination, letting the car have its head at each crossroads. It brought her to high ground, where a few scattered houses had a splendid view of surrounding country-side. Susan and Bob had often talked of buying a house up there, if ever he finished his play and made enough money to afford the acreage required by the zoning law. Bob loved a view.

Today, it was a Christmas card landscape in the cold, bright sun — snow-covered hills, peppered with leafless trees, little, white houses and big, red barns, all under a clean, blue sky.

She passed twin gate-posts. There was a mail-box with the name *Trumbull*. Her foot slammed on the brake. She backed the car a few feet, so she could turn into the driveway she had almost passed.

It was a handsome place. The drive wound between big trees, scattered across a rolling lawn, like a park. There were rustic seats, under copper beeches and oaks, where you could sit on a summer's day with iced tea, or gin and tonic, and look at the roofs of villages and little towns, far below.

The house itself was vine-covered stone, long and low and spacious.

The cold wind of the heights buffeted Susan as she stepped out of the warm car to ring the bell. There was no answer until the third ring. Then the door opened abruptly. "Why, Sue Lundy! Won't you come in?"

She had expected a nurse, but this was Kate Trumbull herself. The psychiatrist had been right about one thing: She was wearing a dressing gown. But could you call it "slopping around?" The gown was warm, plushy nylon, in a pretty shade of rose, bound with satin ribbon to match, and she wore gilt slippers. Two years ago, her hair had been a fashionable auburn, elaborately scrolled and rosetted and fluffed. Now it was candidly grey, straight and short, the hair of an old woman.

Her smile was like the pink glow of sunset softening some ancient, grey ruin. Susan thought: Here is a woman who has looked at Medusa's head, but who was not fortunate enough to be turned into stone. She is still alive and capable of suffering.

Aloud Susan said: "I hope I'm not disturbing you?"

"Not at all. I was having coffee. Come in and have a cup."

The long skirt of her dressing gown flowed with an especially feminine grace around her feet, as she led the way to a breakfast room. How much of the essential feminine modern woman lost with her little-girl frocks and their revelation of legs that were not always as slender as little girls'.

The breakfast table was round with a cushioned window-seat on one side, chairs on the other side. From the chairs, you looked through the window, which was really a curved glass wall, to the Christmas card view below. A tray, with a silver coffee set, stood on the table. There were books and papers scattered on the window seat.

Kate poured a cup of coffee for Susan.

"Thank you," said Susan. "Are you alone?"

"I'm always alone, thank God!, since I got rid of that psychiatrist and his damned nurse."

"How did you get rid of them?"

"There's only one way to get rid of people like that. I told them I was broke and couldn't afford either one of them any longer. It was charming to see how rapidly their interest in my occupational therapy diminshed then."

"What do you do with your time now?"

"I'm teaching myself ancient Greek. I've always wanted to read the tragic poets in the original and there's nothing like purely cerebral exercise to take your mind off your heart. Psychiatry seems to believe that only manual labor has virtue, but I disagree. Satan finds work for idle minds to do . . . Now, we've talked enough about me. How's Bob? And the children? You're so lucky to have a husband, who is so devoted to you and to them!"

Susan began to tremble. It was something she could not control, any more than she could control the tears that slid out of the corners of her eyes, dispassionately as raindrops sliding down a window pane. It was a new kind of crying. No sobs, no sounds, no pursed eyes or twisted mouth. Her face was as still as if she were not crying at all. The water just welled and dropped from her eyes like some sort of mechanical leak that had nothing to do with the emotions.

"Oh, my dear!" Kate was on her feet, taking both Susan's hands in hers. "What is it? You can tell me anything."

Then the whole story came tumbling out.

"What shall I do?" cried Susan. "My mother and father are dead. So are Bob's parents. There's nobody who will help. The responsibility is all mine and it's not just me who's involved — there are the children. Their whole future depends on what I decide to do during this next week. In trouble, I've always turned to Bob. Especially trouble that had to do with the children. But now he's the one I'm trying to protect them from. He's not on our side any more. I can't believe it's happening."

"Hush! Emotion never helps. What a pity that you love him!"

"What do you mean?"

"If only you didn't, you'd have no trouble holding him at all.

"Being in love is like being drunk. It warps your judgment. It makes you give way to grief, anger, jealousy — all the unattractive emotions. The women who deal most successfully with men, whether wives or mistresses, are the women who never feel love for men quite as you and I do. Don't you understand? A sober man can always outwit a man who is drunk and the loveless will always outwit the loving. There's quite a lot of evidence that most prostitutes are frigid and many of them Lesbian. How could they stand their impersonal relationship with men, if they loved men?"

"I thought a prostitute was supposed to be just a man without a penis — a woman who enjoyed sex without love, the way so many men do, and who had no desire for children."

"That inverted male, female only in body, never existed," said Kate. "In the mammalian female, sex and love and motherhood are all of a piece. Women can never stop after the first step in the reproductive process and be happy. Unfortunately, many men can."

"Then Theodore Reik was right when he said that man and woman are so different in their ideas about sexual love that they seem to belong to different species?"

"Perhaps they do. The physiological and emotional differences between the sexes are greater than those between many species. There's a difference in function and in biochemistry. Here. Dry your eyes." Kate handed Susan a box of Kleenex. "You look awful."

"I feel awful. Oh, Kate, what shall I do?"

"First of all, try to get rid of the idea that this has to be true love Bob feels for Kyra — the kind he still feels for you and his children. It may be true love he feels for Kyra, but you can't afford to believe that now, or you'll lose your mind. And there's a good chance that it is not true love at all."

"Then what is it?"

"A mirage — an hallucination. Did you know that glamour means witchcraft in Scotland? Yet we use the word today to describe bitchcraft. Maybe they're the same. I've always suspected that primitive man associated magic with women because he feared woman's sexual power over the unconscious. After all an erection is a motor automatism — a manifestation of the pure unconscious. Because of this, man lives more at the mercy of the unconscious than women. You know the legend of the man who visits an enchanted castle to free the bewitched prisoners there? To free them, he must break the enchanter's crystal and, the moment he does, he sees that the palace is really a pigsty. All that had seemed palatial was only glamour."

"How do you break an enchanter's crystal?"

"Bob's belief in her love for him is her crystal. As long as that remains intact, nothing will break her spell. You must wait."

"That takes strength."

"In a struggle like this, the woman who wins is the woman with the greater inner strength and that has little to do with love. How old is Bob?"

"Fifty-two."

"Flaws that have withstood every other shock and strain in life will split under the impact of the menopause in man as in woman."

"Why? Glands?"

"Partly, and partly the sudden realization that the sands are running out — that we are not immortal. A young man's love is the love of life. An old man's love is the fear of death. The middle-aged man with a young woman on his arm is like the middle-aged woman, who dyes her hair and wears flowered hats. She doesn't look younger, but she feels younger. She doesn't fool others, but she fools herself.

"Death is a slow process. Hair and nails can gow in the grave. *Rigor mortis* has been called the death struggle of muscle, yet it comes after breathing has ceased. Spiritually, people die years before all that, when they first begin to fear old age."

"Would it help Bob if he went to a psychiatrist?"

"In the first place, he wouldn't want to. He doesn't want to be cured of this love for Kyra. He's enjoying it. In the second place, it would depend on the psychiatrist. A lot of them are what is called 'permissive' these days. *So you want to commit murder? Fine! Go right ahead! What's stopping you?* At this point the Freudian analyst assumes that man's own conscience, or super-ego, will guide him in the direction that is best for him and society. The analyst is a priest without a religion, who takes a far more optimistic view of human nature than any religion has ever done. That's why marriage counsellors have appeared on the scene. Because psychiatrists aren't interested in preserving marriages."

"Am I just to sit still with folded hands while Kyra beats me to death?"

"You must take the beating, but you mustn't die. Sometimes these affairs are like an attack of measles, painful and high fevered, while they last, but suddenly over, leaving the patient weak. That's why delay is your only chance. Don't get a divorce. Compromise and wait and hope and pray. Above all, keep it from the children, if you can. As long as they don't know, something has been saved from the wreck. Once they know, all is lost and it hardly matters whether you divorce or not."

"But there are moments when divorce seems the easiest way out."

"Of course there are. We all have moments of defeatism.

But look well before you leap. First, the children. You'll have all the responsibility of bringing them up and you'll have to do it on half the income you would have had otherwise. In a few years, they will be off to college and you will be alone for the rest of your life. Their relation with their father will be maimed.

"Have you ever seen the divorced father with visiting privileges and his children wandering around New York, like lost souls in limbo, never really communicating with each other? A father is someone who's there when you need him — when your temperature is so high your mother is afraid to look at the thermometer, or your geometry problem is beyond her capacity, or there's something too heavy for her to carry for you. A father isn't just someone who takes you to restaurants and theatres two or three times a year, like a rich Australian uncle; someone who cares so little for your mother that he never sees her.

"My psychiatrist told me to explain to the children that their father's relation with me had changed, but not his relation with them. Can you ever change your relation with a child's mother and not change your relation with the child, too? The children of divorce would be happier if they believed their fathers dead. As a matter of fact, you might be less unhappy if Bob were dead."

"Oh, no!"

"Think of all the sympathy you'd get from everybody — all the letters of condolence. This way all you get is pity, a form of contempt, the feeling we all have for the failures in life. You're a little like the unfrocked priest, the disbarred lawyer, the author whose best book is rejected by his favorite publisher. Marriage is your job and it's gone. In an age where every profession fights for tenure, wives and legitimate children are losing theirs."

"It's still unreal," said Susan. "Only two years ago Bob and I sat outside a hospital room, holding hands, and waiting to hear if Buzz would live, or die of polio. Who would have thought that bond could be broken? It's a crude soap-opera touch, isn't it? Buzz just getting over polio and then — this."

"Where do you think soap operas get their raw material? From life. It's not the facts they present that are so crude — it's the artless presentation of those facts.

"Actually, I think Buzzy's polio was a logical part of the whole pattern. Bob suffered fear and shock and, then, the drudgery of a long, hard illness, when almost all your attention was settled on Buzz and the whole household was disrupted. Buzz himself became cranky and nobody could really punish him because he was ill. Be realistic. That sort of thing does not make home attractive to the best of men. It's unpleasant. Men like a comfortable life, which usually means one woman giving them one hundred per cent of her attention, just as a psychiatrist does to his patient."

"If only I had not discovered Bob and Kyra together, it might have gone on for years!"

"A fool's paradise?"

"Perhaps the only paradise is the fool's paradise. Certainly it's better than hell."

"And a gentleman is a man who lies to his wife? And a lady is a wife who is not too curious?"

Susan looked beyond Kate to the distant roofs of the village. "I wish she was dead."

"Would you want him back just because she wasn't there any more? Not because he wanted you?"

"I don't know. Kate, I'm a less nice person than I was before this happened. Now I know that I really never hated anyone before."

"And you have sadistic fantasies about inflicting physical

punishment on her? I know. I've been there, too. That's one reason I've always believed that Jack the Ripper was a woman, who had lost her husband to a prostitute. What man would inflict such gruesome violence on a prostitute? Men like prostitutes.

"He was supposed to be a medical student, because he showed familiarity with female anatomy. Every woman is familiar with her own body. He was never caught, because no pre-Freudian policeman could associate such obscene cruelties with the Victorian idea of woman — fainting, smelling salts and all that. But I see Jacqueline the Ripper in bonnet and shawl, hiding her knife in her reticule, or the folds of her long, flowing skirt, gliding past the policemen, unnoticed and unremembered. The Invisible Woman . . ."

"Kyra isn't even pretty."

"Such women rarely are. Beauty is a warning, like the rattlesnake's rattle. It puts men on guard. But a plain, dumpy, little thing, with no obvious attractions, can sneak up on them."

"Maybe she is pretty," said Susan. "How do I know? I can't judge her, on her looks, with any detachment. Maybe he really loves her and she really loves him and everything I've told you is a distortion of reality."

"That's defeatist, masochistic — stop it! Why should you care if she loves him or not? Whom he loves is all that matters."

"Bob is a very lovable person."

"To you, he is. To her, he's man twenty years older than she is."

"Does that matter? Really?"

"Most girls who believe themselves in love with a man that much older are looking for a father-image. Significantly, they never find a father-image in an older man who has no money."

"That doesn't mean they are gold-diggers necessarily," argued Susan. "A father has to be strong enough to protect you and, in organized society, money is strength."

"That's not love."

"Isn't it?"

"No, it's just romantic sex. You can't really love anyone you haven't known a long time. There's no such thing as love at first sight. That's just a phrase for sex at first sight."

Susan rose. "Is there nothing I can do but wait?"

"I can think of only one thing. You say the girl has a father in New York. You might try talking to him. Not that he'll help you. Even if he disapproves of her conduct, he'll be on her side, because she's his daughter. Even if he's against divorce in principle, he'll probably be delighted to have his daughter marry a man as solvent as Bob, and so he'll do all he can to promote the divorce. But — if you talk to him — you'll find out more about her. As it is, you know nothing. She's just a shadow, a name. You don't know her history, her weaknesses or her strengths. You don't even know if there are any other men in her life. How can you fight in the dark?"

"It would be hard for me to talk to a complete stranger about this."

"You'll have to do many things much harder before this is over. You're fighting for your life and, perhaps, for Bob's life, too — for his long-range happiness, to say nothing of your children. So that means no holds are barred this side of murder. I know, because I fought your battle and lost. The advice I'm giving you is the ruthless advice of someone who was defeated by not being quite ruthless enough."

"I'll do it." Susan's mouth firmed. "I'll do anything. I'll see Kyra's father in New York Monday morning. Thank you,

Kate. You've done me a little good. No one can do me much good now."

Kate came with her to the door, put an arm around her shoulders, kissed her cheek.

"Good luck, fellow traveller!" she said.

As Susan drove away, the words reverberated in her mind's ear. This common agony of hers and Kate's was like a place where two travellers had happened to arrive at the same time, though their pasts and their futures were widely separated. Yes, life was a long journey on foot, a pilgrimage on a steep, winding road. Here and there were flowery meadows and sunny days. Here and there were barren mountains and bitter storms that darkened the sky to a counterfeit night.

No fellow-traveller stayed with you on this journey all the way. Even your children grew and changed and went away on their own journeys. For a few days, or months, or years, your steps marched with this one, or that one, but not forever. Always, sooner or later, you came to the fork in the road where you had to part.

Was this the fork in the road where she had to say goodbye to Bob? Were they fellow-travellers no longer? She had thought that, when the time came, she would die in his arms, or he in hers, but now, perhaps, when she came to the very end of the long road, she would be alone.

At the house, Susan looked up the name *Novacz* in the Manhattan telephone book. Daniel, that was the father's name. Kyra had mentioned it. The address was on Riverside Drive. Kyra had said he was in Washington, but he would be back Monday morning.

Susan closed the telephone book. "I'll be waiting on his doorstep," she told herself. "I'll leave as soon as the children have gone to school."

CHAPTER EIGHT

As NIGHT FELL the view of Park Avenue from the hotel windows looked more than ever like a backdrop. Building silhouettes were palpably flats, pierced with oblong slots all illumined by the same strong bulb backstage to simulate lighted windows. Overhead, the flies were a deep, mysterious blue. One silver-shaded proscenium light cast a speck of glitter on high that looked almost like a real star.

On one of the twin beds, Kyra lay on her side, knees drawn up towards chest, arms crossed over breasts and cheek on pillow — the defensive posture of humanity retreating to the womb. Her hair was tousselled and there were tear-stains on her cheeks, but her eyes were dry now and her face blank with exhaustion.

Bob paced the floor, cigarette in hand. The ash-tray on the centre table overflowed with butts and powdered ash. Smoke hung in visible layers; no one had thought to open a window.

The bottle of scotch was empty, but he had never been more sober in his life. He was in that rare state of extreme stress where mind and body are able to resist the usual power of alcohol.

Kyra broke silence in her smallest voice. "You do forgive me, darling Bob?"

"Of course." He looked at her gravely, the lines around his mouth deeper than ever before. "Your terrible childhood explains your marriage." But, even as he said the words, he heard in his own mind, a far-away echo of Susan's voice: *You really don't know anything about her, do you?*

"And you understand why I just couldn't tell you I was married until now?"

"I'm trying to understand."

"But, Bob, you must understand!"

She sat up on the bed, cross-legged, with a sudden surge of physical energy. She ran both hands through her hair, pushing back the tangles, as if they clogged her thinking processes and dulled her eloquence.

"I loved you the moment I saw you. I felt that we were meant to be together. But, if I had told you I was married, then, in the beginning, you would have sheered off. Men do. They don't like to get into sticky situations. It was bad enough that you had a wife yourself, but, if you had known, in the beginning, that I had a husband as well, you just wouldn't have let things go so far. You would have pulled back while there was still time. You could have, too. Your emotions were not as deeply involved in the beginning as mine were. I needed you. I wanted you. I loved you, so . . . I lied to you. Or, rather, I just didn't tell you the truth about me, because I loved you so much and I was so desperately afraid of losing you."

She slid off the bed. She had kicked off her shoes some time ago. Now, in stocking feet, she ran silent-footed across the thick carpet and slid her arms around his neck, bringing his face close to hers, but not so close that they could not see each other in focus.

"My darling, my dearest . . . I have never loved anyone as I love you. No other man has ever made me feel as you make me feel. If I had to do it all over again, I would do the same thing. It's worth it."

Now her face moved slowly closer and they kissed. But, in a moment, she drew back. "You do understand? Now?"

"Yes. I think so."

She kissed him again, lingering this time. It was he who suddenly moved away.

"Okay. We've talked enough about that. There's no point in talking any more. You didn't tell me, so — here we are, helplessly in love with one another, and two divorces on our hands, instead of one. I know Susan will be a good sport in the long run. She won't do anything nasty. But what about Novacz? Will he give you a divorce? Or will he fight?"

Kyra sat down on the edge of the bed. "I'm afraid he'll fight."

"A contested divorce means scandal," said Bob. "I could lose my job. Public relations is a sensitive area. K., K., D., and V. don't like their employees to carry on like their clients. And any scandal would be hell for Sue and the children."

Kyra bent her head, pleating her skirt between her fingers. Bob paused in his pacing to watch her.

"You realize, of course, that if Novacz is vindictive he might divorce you immediately, naming me as co-respondent as publicly as possible?"

"I don't think he would do that."

"Why not?"

"Because he needs me. He's an old man. I'm the only woman, who . . . excites him."

Bob felt a hot surge of animal jealousy. For one red instant, he hated Kyra. Then it was gone.

"So you think he'll fight to keep you?"

"I'm sure of it. But I don't know how he'll fight. He might threaten us with scandal. If he does, we'll have to call his bluff. I think it more likely he'll just sit tight and say 'No divorce,' expecting me to come back to him when I find there's no hope of marrying you."

"If you're right about him, it narrows our future down to two alternatives: we can go on as we are, meeting now and then, more or less secretly, while we live in our own homes, or we can just cut and run to South America."

"What could we live on there?"

"God knows! Even if you and I could manage there, I couldn't do that to Sue and the children. Because I'd never make enough there to support them, too."

"So you want to just go on as we are?"

"I don't want to, and I don't think it will work for any length of time, if we do. Either one of the four of us will crack under the strain, or our love will die from malnutrition."

"That's not going to happen!" Kyra was on her feet. "It can't happen! It mustn't! Not to us! This isn't just passing fancy or infatuation. This is real. I am the one great love of your life, and you are the one great love of my life, and nothing else matters. Nothing, nothing, nothing . . ."

She threw herself on him like an animal, clinging, scratching, biting, as if all her appetites had fused into one — hunger for Bob.

At last, she collapsed, sobbing, against his shoulder. "We

are not going on just as we are! We're not! We're not!"

He held her, looking beyond the head on his shoulder.

"What else can we do," he said, dully, "if Novacz refuses a divorce?"

She lifted her face, so she could look into his eyes. Her own eyes were blazing. Even her breath was hot against his cheek. She whispered: "Kill him."

"Kyra!" Bob thrust her away from him. "You're out of your mind."

"Am I? Thousands of men and women have killed for love. Why shouldn't we, if there's no other way? Don't we love as much as they did?"

"Now, wait a minute." Bob deliberately made his voice as matter of fact as possible. "That isn't love. It's passion, warped and perverted. Love is creative. It doesn't destroy. It doesn't kill. It gives life and nurtures it. I could not kill another human being."

"You would in a war, even if your country's cause was unjust. More people are killed by modern cars than by wars. Human life is not half so precious to us as we like to pretend. Dada is old and diabetic. He'll die in a year or so anyway. Why can't he die now, before it's too late for us?"

"Kyra." Bob's hands gripped her shoulders until it hurt her. "Stop talking that way, or you will kill my love for you. The only reason you have not done so already is simply that, now I know your history, I can make allowances for you. After all, you were a war orphan, running wild in the streets, in terror of both Russians and Germans. You saw people killed before your eyes, at an age when most American children think that's something that happens only on TV. So I can forgive you for thinking of killing as a way out of a desperate situation, in a moment of passion. But I couldn't forgive you if you went on, in cold blood, urging, arguing and planning such a thing for any length of time. For then you simply wouldn't be the person I love. It would be a case of mistaken identity."

His hands fell away. She sat on the edge of the bed again, her body slack, her head bent, her shoulders drooping. Again she spoke, in her smallest voice. "It would be so easy. No one would ever know."

"What do you mean?"

"If he died from lack of insulin . . . or from an overdose . . . everyone would think it was an accident."

Something hit Bob from that dark region of the mind that is older than conscience, yet not so primitive that it cannot reason. What she said was true. It would be easy. No one would ever know. It would solve all their difficulties. What a fool a man was to put his life between two desperate people and their happiness . . .

"Kyra, we just mustn't think about it. You've already said things that should never have been said. Do you realize what would happen to our love now, if Novacz really did die from an accidental overdose of insulin? I would always think you had done it, and you would always think I might have managed some way to do it for you. How could we love and live together when each suspected the other of a crime like that? Better watch those insulin doses of his carefully from now on, or we'll lose each other."

She smiled, and her whole personality seemed to change. Now she was again the simple-hearted girl he loved so much. "Darling." Her voice was normal again, too. "You know I wouldn't really do a thing like that, don't you?"

"You certainly sounded as if you meant it, a moment ago."

"It was just . . . a sudden impulse."

"That's what every murderer says. But, if you ever yielded

to such an impulse now, it would not be unpremeditated. You'd have had time to think it over."

"Only your testimony could prove that, and you wouldn't testify against me."

"So I'd be an accessory before the fact for your sake? You really do believe in my love, don't you?"

He was teasing her and she knew it. "I do," she said. "I always shall. The way I believe in my love for you."

"God, it's smoky in here!" Bob spoke with cheerful relief, like a man waking from a bad dream. "Let's raise a window and start thinking about dinner."

He lingered by the window inhaling the cold, fresh air, as Kyra put on her shoes and emptied ash-trays. "Are we dining here?" she asked him.

He turned back into the room. "Let's not. Let's have one drink up here and then go to the best restaurant in New York."

"What's the best restaurant in New York?"

"That's a debatable question. Let's try the top ten in the next few days and find out for ourselves."

"Oh, dear, I don't have an evening dress!"

"You look fine as you are. You look more than fine. You look good enough to eat, yourself. You know I've just decided something. You're beautiful. Really beautiful."

Her smile became a low, delicious laugh, as if she were being tickled. The ego responds to titillation quite as eagerly as the body for, like the body, it is usually starved for love.

"I won't be a moment," she said at the bedroom door. "I'm going to change my dress."

Bob went over to the telephone. "Room service . . . This is 1404. We'd like two very dry, double Gibsons, please . . ."

Kyra came out of the bedroom, wearing mink-brown taffeta

with short sleeves and a bouncy, full skirt. It had been designed for women who like to match their dresses to their
furs. With Kyra's black cloth coat, it made a drab combination and Bob found himself thinking, involuntarily, that Kyra
did not have Sue's clothes sense. Sue loved color and line and
understood them. Kyra seemed to choose her clothes with as
much inattention as the average man. She wore as few underclothes as possible in a northern climate and she always slept
nude, as if something fundamentally uncivilized in her re-
sented clothes, both physically and aesthetically. How different
from Susan who loved lacy, transparent nightgowns in all the
pretty pastel shades. Who was it said that the Greeks veiled
their bodies suggestively in moments of passion while Roman
lust preferred its bitchmeat raw?

He made an effort to check this trend of thought. Never
were comparisons more odious than when you compared in-
timacies with two different women, even if the comparison
was only in your own mind. Possibly because the very comparison of sexual memory with sexual actuality was itself a re-
minder that no love lasts forever, that this, too, will pass . . .
And you cannot admit that when you are in love. You
wouldn't be in love, if you did . . .

Above the dull dress, Kyra's face looked rosy and young and
happy, eyes sparkling and lips freshly painted with one of the
pale, coral lipsticks that had just come into fashion. Her
straight, brown hair was sleek and neat as a little girl's when
she goes to her first party. Bob found himself thinking how
very young she was and helpless and dependent on him. It
was almost as if he had found another daughter, who looked
up to him and loved him, without reserve or criticism, as
Robin used to do when she was six.

The waiter's knock roused him. He signed the check and

tipped the man and they sat by the open window, sipping the icy, bitter drinks. Outside, the spotlit street scene was darker and some of the actors, who had parts without lines, were pretending to walk their dogs or hurry home from their work. In order to establish the authentic mood of a street scene, there was even one actor costumed as a policeman twirling his nightstick as he tried the doors of small shops closed for the night.

Bob's glance followed that tall, solid figure in blue. "Kyra, before we leave this room, I want one thing clearly understood. Never again are you to think, let alone say, any of the things you said about Novacz this afternoon. Promise?"

"Of course, Bob. I was a little crazy, I guess."

"It's not enough for us never to mention it again. We must never even think of it again. Thoughts can be dangerous."

"I know, but . . . what are we going to do?"

"We have to take this thing step by step, like everything else in life. It's a mistake to try to look too far ahead, because you can't. There are too many unpredictable factors. We've got to ask Novacz to divorce you. Then, when we have his answer, we go on from there. You may be wrong about him. He may be delighted to get rid of you — you vain, little thing! For all you know, he already has a mistress of his own and he's worrying right now about how to ask you for a divorce."

Kyra laughed, but shook her head. "I wish it were that simple, but I'm sure it isn't — as sure as you can be of anything. So then?"

Bob felt a shock of fear. When he had begun to speak, he had not realized where the words were leading him. Now, suddenly, he saw. If Novacz refused her a divorce, it would be almost impossible for them to meet secretly. Novacz would do all he could to make it impossible, once he knew what was going on, and that meant only one thing: Bob would lose Kyra.

The thought of losing her was unbearable at this moment in his life. She was youth, she was life itself. There would be nothing left. He would have tasted paradise and lost it. But that wasn't all. What really frightened him was the thought of Kyra's own future.

She would have lost her paradise, too. She would be living intimately with a man she hated. A man whose death from an under, or over, dose of insulin could so easily pass as an accident . . .

And if it didn't?

The modern police were scientific and patient . . .

The full horror of his tragedy was now upon him. If Kyra were to die for murdering her husband, how could he bear the rest of his own life? She would not incriminate him. The police might not do so. But he would have to go on living with the knowledge that his love had destroyed her.

"Kyra." His hand on her chin, he turned her face up to his. She smiled, eyes retreating behind the chubby, child-like cushions of her cheeks.

"Swear to me you will never even think of murder again, no matter what happens? For my sake. I couldn't go on living, if you became a murderess for me. Do you understand?"

"I do, Bob. I swear I'll never even think of murder again — no matter what happens."

She repeated the words earnestly, but Bob still had a sense of suffocation, almost claustrophobia. How blindly, how heedlessly, he had walked into this trap and let it close around him. A trap baited cunningly with sex and youth and love and adventure — all the dazzling things in life. But still a trap.

He did not think of Kyra as having set the trap for him. He thought of her as being caught in it with him. And that sense of being caught was so vivid just then, and so nearly unbearable, that he cried out, in anguish:

"Kyra, darling, for your sake as well as mine, I wish I had never met you!"

Her face was still. Even her eyes did not change. She simply looked at him. He could not read her expression at all.

Then she said: "I'm starving. Shall we go?"

"Okay. We'll spend a quiet Sunday here together and we'll see Novacz the first thing Monday morning, when he gets back from Washington."

"It would be better for me to see him alone at first, but I'd like you to be standing by."

"I'll stay right by the telephone in my office until you call me. And now I'm going to call Sue and tell her about Lou Symington and the play. She'll be so pleased."

"Oh?" Kyra didn't look pleased at all just then.

CHAPTER NINE

Susan dressed herself without her usual care Monday morning. It no longer seemed to matter much how she looked. She had always enjoyed the morning routine — taking a bath, putting on shoes and stockings and fresh underwear. Now those little things were just habit, powered by inertia. She chose skirt and blouse at random without regard for the colors. She put on her short, fur jacket, and picked up her handbag without bothering to check it for cash and cigarettes and keys.

It had been the same way at breakfast. She could hardly remember any morning in her adult life when she had not tackled orange juice and eggs and coffee with zest, and seized the morning newspaper with a real appetite for the headlines. Now she forced down coffee, pushed away eggs and left the newspaper unfolded. No matter what they were doing out there, in the great world of nuclear bombs and politicians, it was no concern of hers now.

It's just as if I had died, she thought. I'm the ghost of what I was and I long for the life I lost the way the dead must long for life, if they feel anything at all.

She remembered the few other moments of shock and grief and fear — her parents' deaths, Bob's going off to Korea, the doctor's announcement that Buzz had polio. How different all those had been! There had been tears, but they were clean tears. She had feared losing those she loved, but she had not feared losing their love. That would live on always in her heart, surviving the death of their bodies. This was another kind of death, this annihilation of her faith in Bob's love for her. Her body was alive and healthy, but something else — heart, soul, spirit — whatever you chose to call the thing that told your hands to move and watched the signals from the senses on the switchboard of the brain, that thing was wounded, dying.

As usual the commuters' train reached New York twenty minutes late. It was nearly ten o'clock when she took a taxi and gave the driver the address on Riverside Drive. It was a windy day, with little whitecaps dancing on the broad, grey, river and overhead a leaden sky that threatened rain or snow.

Holding her jacket close around her, bent against the wind, she walked up the steps to the vestibule of the old-fashioned apartment building. She found a row of doorbells and name cards and pressed the doorbell under the card that carried the name "Daniel Novacz." No answer. She should have telephoned for an appointment. How silly to rush into town, trusting to chance that Novacz would be at home whenever she happened to arrive.

Was she too late, or too early? Should she wait here in the cold wind, on the chance that he might still be on his way home from Washington?

A great lassitude swept over her. If she missed him today, she would never be able to summon the nerve for such an interview another time.

Before she turned away, she pressed the button just once more. There was a clicking sound and the door swung open.

She walked into the hallway. The door of a ground floor apartment stood open and a man was in the doorway — tall, thin, old, with a beaky nose and round, hard indignant eyes — the eyes of an eagle.

"Mr. Novacz?"

"Yes?"

"I am Susan Lundy. Robert Lundy's wife."

He smiled warmly. "Oh, Kyra told me she's spending the week-end with you. Is she with you now?"

"No."

His smile died. "Where is she?"

"I don't know. May I come in?"

"Of course, Mrs. Lundy. My apologies. I should not have kept you standing here, but... my mind was wandering. Is Kyra all right?"

"As far as I know. Haven't you seen her this morning?"

"No, I haven't seen her since I left for Washington last Friday."

Susan settled herself in an armchair with a view of the river. She did not feel the awkwardness she had felt yesterday at the very thought of such an interview with a stranger. She cared too little for herself now to care greatly for the opinion of others. She spoke without effort, in a voice as detached as if she were speaking of people she scarcely knew.

"Has Kyra told you anything about my husband and herself?"

Now his face looked as if it had never smiled. "Is there anything to tell?"

"Then she hasn't."

"No, she hasn't. But I think I can guess. She wants to marry your husband."

"How did you know?"

"It has happened before. Kyra is not original. She repeats herself. A sign of neurosis, I believe. But she has always been neurotic."

Susan took a deep breath. "And the other times . . . what happened?"

"I was able to keep her from making a fool of herself. I don't know if I can do so again. She's getting older. Older and more desperate."

"You must have more influence over her than most fathers have over their daughters today if —"

"One moment, please, Mrs. Lundy. You are misinformed. It's not the first time Kyra has told this particular lie. I am not her father. I am her husband."

It was the shift of the kaleidoscope on a grand scale. Every piece of the situation moved and fell into a different relationship with every other. But because these pieces were living and human, not just bits of colored glass, it was difficult to take in every aspect of the new pattern at first glance.

"She must be insane," said Susan, at last. "She made Bob believe that all he needed in order to marry her was my consent to his divorce from me. She never mentioned any other obstacle."

"She never does, at that stage."

"Do you want to divorce her?"

"No."

"Does she believe she can persuade you to do so?"

"I doubt it."

"Then what is she after?"

"My dear Mrs. Lundy, I believe it has always been her

desire and intent to have me killed. She's a coward. She won't do it herself. For years she has been looking for a lover with nerve enough to kill me for her sake."

Susan tried to tell herself that this old man was insane himself, such things couldn't happen, then unwillingly, she remembered how many newspaper stories she had read of dissatisfied wives who had given weapons to their lovers and, worse than weapons, words — pleading, cajoling, rationalizing away the ugliness of murder in the name of love.

But it wasn't love. No woman would make a murderer of the man she loved. The risk for him was too great. Such women did not love their lovers at all; they merely hated their husbands.

With an effort, she recovered her voice. "What you are saying is monstrous."

"Kyra is, perhaps, something of a monster. Some people are, you know. It's hard to realize, because it doesn't show visibly. Man believes only what he can see. Such people dress and smile and talk and walk and eat and kiss, like everybody else. But, if we could see their souls, we would shrink from them with far more horror than we now shrink from spastic or Mongoloid."

"What are you going to do?" asked Susan.

"Let me ask you a question first: do you believe your husband capable of murder?"

"No."

"You're very sure, and yet.... Let me ask you another question: would you have believed him capable of infidelity four months ago?"

Susan searched her soul. Four months ago ... no, not even forty-eight hours ago would she have believed him capable of saying to her: *I want to live with her, not with you. ...*

Novacz took her silence as an answer. "You see? Who can ever be sure of another human being? Who ever knows what is really going on behind the mask of smiles, of tears, of kisses? Every human being has a breaking point. We ourselves don't know what is going on in our deep unconscious until it erupts to the surface. The unconscious is like the body. Men can talk and laugh and run about their little affairs for months with no conscious awareness that the traitor body has already surrendered to a cancerous cell. The unconscious can have even more dreadful surprises for the superficial, little ego, who so fondly imagines he is master of his fate and captain of his soul . . . However, it's a chance I have to take."

"What chance?"

"That you're right about your husband. That he really is incapable of murder. So I shall refuse Kyra a divorce on any terms, assuming that she has not found a killer this time, hoping that she is still too cowardly to be a killer herself and that the whole affair will fade out in a few months, as the others did, when she found that I would make another marriage impossible for her."

"And then, in a few months, Bob will come back to me, not because he has made a choice and really wants me, but because he can't have Kyra."

For Bob to become disillusioned with Kyra was one thing, but for Kyra to become unattainable was another. Who could compete with the unattainable?

"Mrs. Lundy, you look white. I am going to give you a glass of wine."

"Thank you."

It was heavy, sweet wine, but it warmed her vitals and spurred her blood to a more normal pace.

"I know what you are thinking," said Novacz. "You don't

want your husband back just because I won't divorce Kyra."

"You're very penetrating, but I'm not sure what I want at this moment."

"And you are wondering why I don't divorce Kyra, since she hates me enough to plot my murder."

Susan had been too self-absorbed to think of his point of view. She could not admit that, so she nodded gravely.

"Let me tell you something about Kyra. During the war our little country was badly torn, like a rabbit savaged by two big dogs, Germany and Russia. I was a Professor of Slavic Languages at the University of Praz, and I also spoke German, so I was able to serve, first, as interpreter for German Head-quarters, and then as interpreter for Russian Headquarters. In short, I collaborated with both sides in turn, the only sensible course for the individual in a world gone mad. I always had food, shelter, clothing and a bearable life, even during the worst crises, while the wretched patriots were being shot or starved to death or dumped in concentration camps.

"When the war was over and the Russians settled down for a nice, long visit with us, peasants, who had flocked to the towns from the scorched earth of their farms, were roaming the streets like the bands of starving, mongrel dogs in Istanbul. The Russians conscripted some, put others on collective farms and so forth, but the children, who had lost their parents, remained running wild in the Old Town — the old part of Praz, where the slums are, and also the University, for it is old, too.

"These children were half-starved, diseased and infinitely corrupt. They had seen and heard and done things which you and I could hardly begin to imagine. The Russians decided to round up these vermin and ship them to some place in Russia — a sort of cross between a reform school and a concentration camp, I imagine, though the children themselves were convinced they would be killed. Why, I don't know. Hysteria, I suppose, and memories of the Nazis.

"Anyway, the night the children were rounded up was a rather terrible night for the Old Town of Praz, which has seen enough terrible nights in the past. After all, Christianity only came to our country five hundred years ago. Before that, there were strange rites involving human sacrifice, which have not been seen in western Europe since Druid days. We are a primitive people, though most of us will not admit it. I'm rather proud of it. I admire primitive qualities.

"Well, no doubt you've guessed what happened. Kyra was one of those children. She was running from Russian soldiers, when she forced the latch of a window in my study and climbed through. She went down on her knees and promised me anything, if I would hide her."

"And you did," said Susan. "That was a brave thing to do, a noble thing."

"My dear lady, I hate to disillusion you, but it was not brave, because I had completely won the trust of the Russians by my active collaboration and it was anything but noble. I was fifty-six years old when Kyra broke into my study. Kyra herself was fourteen. I told you that the children who roamed the streets were infinitely corrupt. It never occurred to Kyra that I would save her out of common humanity, or even as a patriotic gesture against the invader. In her world, no one ever did anything for nothing.

"So she offered me, there, on her knees, the only thing she had. I could take any sexual liberties I pleased with her, she said, and she was clever enough to hint that her experiences in the streets of Praz had taught her many refinements of the sexual relationship, which were unknown to respectable women twice her age.

"The fifties are a vulnerable age for men. My wife was bedridden with a shaky heart. So I hid Kyra from the Russians in my study. . . .

"She fulfilled her part of the bargain. She told me her peasant father had been strict and Puritanical, even by our peasant standards, and I think she was unconsciously defying him in her new life. I was grateful to him. When a man reaches my age, he is not as easily roused to sexuality as a younger man. Kyra's youth and skill and enthusiasm provided such a stimulus that I was capable of performance with her, which I would not have been capable of with any other woman. She still provides that stimulus and that is why I shall not divorce her. Without her, my sexual life would be at an end. I am in my seventies now and I am utterly dependent on her. I don't like her. I don't love her. But I need her."

"Why did you marry her if you don't love her? Just to keep her?"

"Not entirely. My first wife died a few months after Kyra moved into our house. By that time, Kyra no longer had to hide. She was tall for her age and could pass as my housekeeper without anyone suspecting that she was one of the fugitive street children. But I did not marry Kyra then, because I had grown-up children, who would have regarded it as a reflection on their mother's memory.

"At that time, Kyra was my wife in everything but name. She lived with me openly, played hostess at the few little parties I gave, and was accepted by all my close friends who never bothered to ask whether we were married or not.

"When I was appointed to the staff of our chief delegate to the U.N., our Minister of Foreign Affairs sent for me and told me that I could not take Kyra to America unless I married her. Officialdom in the United States would tolerate divorce, but not open adultery. A Spanish Ambassador, many years ago, had tried introducing his mistress to Washington as his wife, with disastrous results. Every member of the staff of our delegation must do everything possible to make a good impression in the United States, even a humble interpreter like myself.

"It all seemed rather silly to me, but I didn't want to miss the chance of living in the United States. Even after the Russians departed, we had nothing like your luxurious standard of living in my poor, little country. So I married Kyra. I had no idea then that I might be signing my own death warrant."

"What do you mean?"

"Kyra, like all those who have starved, loves material comfort, and she never saw it before in such abundance until she came to this country. She wants to stay. She wants to become an American citizen, so she can enjoy all these good things all the rest of her life. As my wife, she has little hope of this. What happens to her if I am recalled? She goes back with me. What happens to her if I die? She has no status here, except as my wife, so that would also mean going back to her own country. Once there, she inherits no money from me. Our law does not compel me to leave her anything, so my small savings are willed to my grown up children, and she knows this. So, in a few moments, my death would reduce her to a life of poverty and hard work, in a country where all comforts are scarce and life is hard and monotonous for all workers.

"Kyra is in her thirties. Her sexual opportunities will be fewer with each year from now on. That's why she wants me to divorce her. That's why she thinks longingly of my death, when I refuse. She believes her only chance of future ease and comfort is to marry an American citizen. Only an American husband can give her the status and money she wants. Only an American husband can establish her here.

"The moment she arrived in the United States as my wife, she began hunting, frantically, desperately, for an American lover, who would love her enough to marry her. Most of her victims were middle-aged, married men, partly because they are the easiest conquests, and partly because her life with me had made her expert in catering to older men.

"She was amazed and furious the first time she found I would not divorce her. My refusal, in each case, slowed up the affair long enough for the man to come to his senses. After several failures she began to think of murder and now, I honestly believe she has reached the point where she is almost ready to kill me herself, if she cannot find a lover who will do the job for her.

"But she is afraid of the police in any country. Remember, for many years she was a child criminal. So she would infinitely prefer that the actual killing was done by her lover . . . just in case the murderer was caught . . ."

Susan was beginning to think of Novacz himself as infinitely corrupt, but she managed to hide her feelings, and keep her voice impersonal, as she said: "So Kyra would rather risk her lover's life than her own?"

"Of course. Haven't you understood anything I've been saying? Kyra is viciously self-centered. But she would not expect her lover to be caught."

"Why not?"

"It would be an accident." Novacz rose and crossed the room to a table by the window. He picked up a small leather case and opened it. "Do you know what that is?"

"An hypodermic syringe."

"I'm a diabetic. I take insulin, self-injected. The dose is precisely measured to suit my individual condition. If I took a little too much — or too little — it would be fatal, but, if I were apparently alone when it happened, who could ever prove, beyond a reasonable doubt, that it was not an accident? I dare say Kyra has already explained all this to your husband."

"How can you bear to live with her?"

"I told you what her hold on me is. If I lose her, I become an old man."

"She might kill you at any moment."

"I watch her carefully. I never give her any opportunities."

"How do you stand it? Always hating each other, always watching each other, in such close quarters?"

"I am not a sentimentalist, Mrs. Lundy. I may, perhaps, shock you if I say I rather enjoy being able to force Kyra to stay with me against her will and fulfill all those promises she made to me on her knees, in my study in Praz, when she was fourteen. You should be glad I feel that way. For it means that Kyra is not free to marry your husband, and, if she cannot marry him, she will soon lose interest in him."

"Or she will kill you. Or she will make Bob do it."

"You said he wouldn't."

"And you said: how can one ever be sure? Everyone has a breaking point." Susan rose. "I suppose I should thank you for being honest with me. I cannot say you have made me any happier."

"You are foolish, like all romantics. In this world, we all have to settle for second-best, sooner or later. There is no Santa Claus and no pot of gold at the end of the rainbow. The small sensualities are what make life bearable. The great passions cause nothing but trouble and tragedy."

"You may be right, but I am afraid I am too old to change."

"Good bye, Mrs. Lundy. The whole thing will be over in a month or so. It's just a matter of time."

A matter of time ... Susan repeated the words to herself

as she walked down Riverside Drive in the rain, looking for a taxi.

Was it that simple? If only Bob hadn't slept with Kyra. Actions don't merely speak louder than words — they shout. A wife can bear all kinds of philandering in her husband, as long as it is confined to words and caresses, but the physical act of sex is strangely as irrevocable as death itself. And, a thing once done, does not slip into the past and disappear. It is always there, a part of the present and even the future. Who was it said the future is simply the past entered by another gate?

It was the irrevocable quality of human action that made life such a desperate game. We make our choices blindfold. Our amnesia for the future gives us the illusion of free will and the idea of good and evil, yet, actually, we cannot control any consequences of any decision we make. There are too many other factors involved besides the decision that sets them all in motion. Yet we hold each other responsible for all the consequences of every decision.

Through a silver veil of raindrops, Susan saw a blurred figure coming towards her, a woman like herself, caught in the rain without an umbrella. Only when they were face to face did Susan recognize her.

"Kyra! Where is Bob?"

"At his office."

"Oh, Kyra, do you remember saying that Bob and I had a happy home? That you felt it the moment you crossed our threshold? How could you say that while you were planning to destroy our happiness forever?"

"But that's just why I want Bob."

"What do you mean?"

Kyra's voice was uninflected and unfeeling as ever, almost as if she were talking in her sleep. "You and Bob were the happiest of all the married couples I knew. That's why I chose Bob."

"And broke up a happy home."

"There wouldn't be any sense in breaking up an unhappy home. I wouldn't want a man who couldn't make his wife happy."

"And you planned for me to discover you with Bob that night, I suppose."

"Of course. I tried to make enough noise to wake you. I pushed the sofa so it would move and the castors would creak, hoping you would hear them and come in to see what was going on. I knew I didn't have a chance unless you found out about us. Then you'd be hurt and jealous and angry and you would destroy yourself. But . . . what are you doing here? I thought you were in Westchester?"

"I've been talking to the man you called your father."

"Is he going to divorce me?"

"No." Susan enjoyed being the first one to tell her so.

"He'll have to! I'll make him! He must! I'll kill him if he doesn't! I'll kill him!" Kyra began to run towards the apartment house.

Susan walked on in the other direction, blinded by rain and tears.

CHAPTER TEN

WHEN SUSAN FORCED her way into an office building through a surge of workers on their way out to lunch, she felt like a swimmer struggling against a strong tide. The new, self-service elevator was empty. When she stepped into the lobby of K., K., D. and V. the receptionist's desk was empty, too. She walked down the corridor to Bob's office and tapped on the door. No answer. She turned the knob and pushed it open. No one there.

She had a moment of hysteria. *She was alone. There was no one else in the office or the building or the whole city by this time. They had all gone . . . elsewhere. And left her alone. She would always be alone now, forever more . . .*

She pulled herself together with an effort almost physical in its tangibility. *Susan, you fool, you're not helping Bob or yourself or anyone else this way . . .*

She walked back to the lobby. The receptionist was just

settling herself into her chair. She looked like an illustration in Vogue. Beehive hair, darkened eyelids, wide, painted mouth, long, red nails to match. A snowy, white blouse with long, full sleeves and a tight, short, black skirt. *The works and then . . . the men fall for Kyra, who looks like . . . well, the daughter of a boarding-house keeper in a small town. It's just a literary convention that a beautiful face and figure combined with studied elegance in dress make a woman irresistible to men. Their needs are psychological, and physical, not visual. All that clothes can do is give a woman confidence in herself.*

"Good morning, Mrs. Lundy!"

"Good morning, Grace. Do you know where Mr. Lundy is? He's not in his office."

"Oh, he hasn't been in at all this morning," said Grace, brightly. "There are a dozen telephone messages for him. He should be in at any moment, but I don't know where he is now."

Susan put one hand on the desk and leaned against it, so weary she had to have some physical support. "Surely you're mistaken. I know he was in his office this morning."

"What makes you think so?"

Susan could not say Kyra Novacz told me so.

Grace went on: "I've been here since nine o'clock and I haven't seen him. He never comes in before nine."

"You weren't here when I came in," said Susan.

"I had just slipped into the powder room for the first time this morning. I've been here right along since nine and I know I would have seen Mr. Lundy, if he had come in. Why don't you wait for him in his office, Mrs. Lundy? He's pretty sure to be in soon."

"Thank you." Susan went back to Bob's office. She sat in his chair, at his desk, and buried her face in her hands. *I can't*

*stand much more, I just can't ... I need a drink, a tranquil-
lizer ...*

But neither of these twentieth century panaceas was handy.
She could only call on her own deepest inner strength. What
was it Kate Trumbull had said? *In a struggle like this, the
woman who wins is the woman with the greater, inner
strength ...*

She caught a glimpse of her own face in the shining surface of a glass-covered picture on the wall. *I look like a
drowned rat.* Out came the comb and the lipstick and the
compact with its little mirror. The line of red she drew around
her lips was uneven. She looked down at her hands. They were
shaking.

She lit a cigarette and forced herself to look out the window
at the passing show. Dull light, filtered through a heavy layer
of clouds, made the whole city dream-like and insubstantial,
but there were two notes of color the dusky light could not
subdue — cars and umbrellas, no longer the uniform black of
her childhood, but gay as a bed of tulips, rose-red, lime-green,
pale blue, mauve — all the rainbow colors.

Each minute was an hour. To kill time, she tried playing a
game with herself, making one point for each red umbrella
she sighted, two points for each red car. She had reached a
score of sixty-one when the telephone rang. As she reached
for it, she glanced at the clock on Bob's desk. One o'clock.

"Hello?" Her voice was hoarse, unrecognizable, as if she
had not used it for a long time and had somehow forgotten
how it ought to sound.

"Bob ..." It was Kyra, breathless, almost panting. "Why
don't you answer me? ... Oh, I suppose Susan is there. I've
bad news. Very bad. Meet me for lunch. Usual place. Usual
time. Don't answer. Just come ... my love ..."

Susan put down the telephone. Almost immediately it rang again.

"Is that Susan? This is Alan Dorfmann. Grace told me you were waiting for Bob in his office. Do you happen to know where Bob is now?"

"No, I don't, Alan. I expected him to be here when I came."

"Did he tell you he would be?"

"No." Again Susan could not say it was Kyra who had told her. "I — I just had that impression."

"Have you any idea where he might be?"

"No, I'm afraid not."

"Well, come on over to my office while you're waiting, I'd like to talk to you."

"Alan, is there something wrong? You sound as if Bob were missing."

"Not missing — just mislaid." Dorfmann laughed heartily at his own joke. "You know where my office is, don't you? If not, Grace will show you the way."

Susan put the telephone down. Obviously, something was wrong. Oh, why couldn't Bob have been in his office this morning, as he always had been on every other Monday morning? Even Kyra had thought he would be.

Susan found Dorfmann's office without consulting Grace. It was too big to miss even in the network of inter-office corridors. She tapped on the door and Dorfmann's voice said: "Come in!"

She opened the door.

"Well, well, Sue, you look as fresh as a daisy!" Dorfmann spoke before he had taken a good look at Susan's ravaged face. Once he had done so he looked as if he couldn't quite make up his mind whether he should venture the conventional, show-business greeting of a casual kiss or not. He compromised by patting her shoulder as he pulled out a chair for her.

Susan said: "You look worried."

"I am . . . a little." Dorfmann's facile smile died suddenly. "Bob and I had an appointment with the publicity director of Tantamount this morning at eleven. Bob didn't show. And he didn't telephone. That's not like him, you know."

"No, it's not a bit like him."

"Maybe you and I can figure out where he is. Any ideas?"

"I'm afraid not. I'm sort of marooned in the country, you know, especially since Buzz had polio. I've lost all track of Bob's associates in town."

"And that is a pity." Dorfmann's gaze was direct, unsmiling. "Bob has been behaving rather oddly in the last few weeks. Have you noticed it at home?"

"No." What else could she say? "Just what do you mean?"

Dorfmann's glance dropped, focussed on his blotter. "It's as if his mind were on something else, not his work. And more than that. As if he were living in another world where K., K., D. and V. don't exist."

"You mean he's been neglecting his work?"

"No. Oh, no. He goes through the motions faithfully. But . . . he's just not there. It's as if he were living in a dream . . . acting out a fantasy that is far more real to him than reality."

Susan could not trust her voice to speak.

Dorfmann went on. "Do you think a vacation would do him any good? A Caribbean cruise or something like that?"

Susan shook her head. "I'm afraid it's too late for that."

"Too late?"

Susan had not meant to say so much. Now she tried to backtrack. She picked her words gingerly. "I have noticed that he was not quite himself lately, but I don't believe a vacation would help. He'd have to go alone. I couldn't leave Buzz."

"Why not? There's usually a relative or a friend, who can take over for a few weeks in these cases. There are even a few nursemaids and housekeepers left in this servantless world. They're expensive, but . . . in an emergency . . ."

Susan's heart quailed. He knows. He knows everything. And he's trying to help.

"I'll think it over," she said. "Maybe it is a good idea."

"I'm sure it is." Dorfmann's glance caught hers and held it. "Do you happen to know a girl name Kyra Novacz?"

"Slightly." Susan's voice was not encouraging.

"Bob introduced her?"

"Yes." Susan didn't elaborate.

"Do you know who she is? Where she comes from?"

"Some little country in eastern Europe. Her father has a job with the U.N. and —"

Dorfmann's telephone interrupted her. He snatched it impatiently. "Grace, I told you I was not to be disturbed . . . What? Casovitz? . . ." His face changed. "Good God, are you kidding? . . . Okay, I suppose I'll have to see him, but keep him out there for another five minutes — if you can."

Dorfmann slammed the telephone back in its cradle and turned on Susan with a desperate urgency. "Sue, get back to Bob's office and wait there till I call you. No, not that door! Take this side door, so you don't have to go past Grace's desk and —"

The main door opened without a warning knock. The man who stood on the threshold was tall, broad of shoulder and thigh, with a thick neck and a wide, flat face. There was a lot of bone and muscle there, but there was also a ruthless intelligence in the small, still eyes and tight mouth.

Susan felt cold as if the very presence of this man had lowered the temperature of the room. He was not a man paying a social call and he was certainly not a client of K., K., D., and V. He was . . . she searched her mind for a descriptive word . . . he was an inquisitor. Someone like an income tax investigator or an FBI man, the passive, heartless tool of some organization more powerful than himself.

Dorfmann tried to recreate a normal social atmosphere. "See you later, Sue. This won't take long, will it, Lieutenant?"

But the man was not looking at Dorfmann. His eyes were on Sue. "Mrs. Robert Lundy?"

In sheer surprise, Susan blurted: "How did you know?"

"The receptionist said you were in here with Mr. Dorfmann. Have you any idea where your husband is, Mrs. Lundy?"

"Not at the moment. Why do you want to know? Who are you?"

"This is Lieutenant Casovitz of the New York Police Department," said Dorfmann.

"When did you last see your husband, Mrs. Lundy?"

Susan had to have time. She looked at Dorfmann. "Why is Lieutenant Casovitz asking me these questions, Alan?"

Dorfmann's glance switched to Casovitz. "I think you should tell her, Lieutenant."

"Who's conducting this investigation, you or me?" snapped the Lieutenant. "When did you last see your husband, Mrs. Lundy?"

It was a blunder, this display of habitual, uncalculated rudeness. For it roused Susan's temper and braced her backbone.

"If you are conducting an investigation, Lieutenant Casovitz, I believe I should have legal advice before I answer questions, especially those concerning my husband. What are you investigating, and why?"

The Lieutenant behaved like a man whose bluff has been called when he did not expect it. He spoke a little less brutally.

"Mrs. Lundy, have you ever heard of a man called Daniel Novacz?"

"Yes."

"This man has been murdered. I am in charge of the investigation. I am interviewing everyone who knew Novacz. Now will you tell me where your husband is? He is the only friend of Novacz I have been unable to find."

Susan must have whitened for she felt Dorfmann's arm around her shoulders, holding her tight, giving her what moral support a friendly, human contact could.

"Murdered. . . ." The word came out like a gasp. "When?"

"This morning, between ten and twelve, according to medical evidence. His skull was fractured by a heavy paperweight from his own desk. Do you understand why I want to find your husband? He was expected here this morning, but he has not been in his office and no one knows where he is."

"My husband?" Astonishment sent Susan's voice climbing. "You are not suggesting for one moment that Bob is capable of —"

"Then why has he disappeared?" The Lieutenant's voice suggested a weary cynicism. "Let's not beat around the bush, Mrs. Lundy. Do you, or do you not, know of the relationship between your husband and Daniel Novacz' wife, Kyra?"

Again Susan fought for time. "What do you mean?"

"I think you know perfectly well that it was a relationship which gave your husband a strong motive for killing Daniel Novacz. Don't you?"

Susan's chin rose. "I have not the slightest idea what you are talking about. My husband is devoted to his home and his children."

"Oh, come, Mrs. Lundy, that sort of talk won't do you or your husband any good. I've just questioned the bellboys, elevator men and floor waiters at a certain hotel not too far from here. Though Mrs. Novacz and Mr. Lundy were registered separately this week-end, they arrived together and departed together and shared meals and drinks in Mrs. Novacz' suite. There's no doubt as to what their relationship was in my mind and there'll be no doubt in the minds of judge and jury when he comes to trial."

"Then all you've really got so far against Bob is motive?"

"That's important. In law, you don't need to prove motive to get a conviction, but you cannot convince a jury without one."

"Why do you put it all on Bob?" Susan cried out vehemently. "If all this is true, someone else had a powerful motive — Kyra Novacz herself."

"She has been through this twice before. All their friends know. Twice she has asked Novacz for a divorce and twice he has refused. Obviously a lady with a second marriage on her mind. But neither time did she try to kill her husband. Why should she kill him now?"

"Her hatred of him may have been accumulating," said Susan. "The third time was just more than she could bear. Have you questioned her?"

"We haven't been able to find her either."

"She called my husband's office on the telephone only a few minutes ago. He wasn't there, so I answered."

It seemed as if every muscle in the Lieutenant's body contracted. He almost quivered with the alert hunger of the hunting animal that scents its prey.

"What did she say?"

"She thought she was talking to Bob. She didn't recognize my voice. She said she had bad news. She wanted Bob to meet her for lunch."

"Where? When?"

"She said the usual place, at the usual time."

"You know where?"

"No."

"Someone must know!" The Lieutenant looked at Dorfmann.

"If I did know, I wouldn't tell you," said Dorfmann.

"You could be arrested for withholding evidence!"

"I doubt it. Besides, I don't know. Or, rather —" Dorfmann grinned. "You can't prove I do know."

"Can't I? You wait here. Both of you."

The Lieutenant was gone. He hadn't slammed the door, but, somehow, his very silence was noisy.

Susan turned to Dorfmann. "Thank you, Alan, but . . . Oh, what shall we do now?"

"Get Bob a lawyer right away. He may be arrested at any moment."

"Whom would you recommend?"

"The best criminal lawyer is Lee Marienberg, but he costs the earth."

"We can manage the money somehow. Wasn't it Disraeli who said: 'First decide what you want to do; then — and only then — look around for the money to do it with'?"

"Easier said than done." Dorfmann dropped his eyelids, lifted them and gave Susan a sad, shamefaced look. "I hate to say this, doll, but I think I should say it now. If Bob is arrested, he will lose his job."

"Oh . . ." Susan was shaken as if he had struck her.

"If I were the boss here, I'd keep him on. But I'm only one of four partners, and a junior partner at that. I can be outvoted and I will be. K., K., D., and V. are chicken when it comes to adverse publicity for the firm itself."

Susan pressed her lips together. "Whether he's fired or not, he must have the best lawyer in New York.

"There's the play. Lou Symington is going to produce it as a movie. Surely Bob can get a cash advance from her."

"Now?"

"She was enthusiastic about it, Bob said. He was so excited he called me Saturday. Why don't we call her now?"

Susan reached for the telephone on Dorfmann's desk, but he forestalled her. "Let me call. Let her think I'm Bob's business manager. More impressive."

Dorfmann got an outside line and dialled. "Miss Symington, please . . . Alan Dorfmann . . . No, I'll wait . . ." He picked up a pencil and began drawing on his memo pad — women's feet in high-heeled shoes. "Lou, darling?" Dorfmann dropped the pencil and leaned back in his chair, the telephone nuzzling him between cheek and shoulder. "Fine, and how are you? And lover-boy? . . . I'm calling for Bob Lundy . . . Yes, I'm acting for him in business matters. I know you're crazy about this terrific play of his you're making into a movie and I wanted to bring up something Bob's too unbusiness-like to think of — the little matter of a cash advance — and —"

Susan could hear a staccato squeaking that was all the telephone made of Lou's velvet voice at the distance of a few feet. The squeaking went on and on and on. Dorfmann took the telephone away from his ear and looked at it as if it were an obscene object. It was still squeaking when he replaced it in its cradle, breaking the connection without a word of leave-taking to Lou.

"I was afraid of that." He looked at Susan. "She heard the one o'clock news on radio. She knows that Daniel Novacz was murdered and that the police want Robert Lundy for questioning, so . . . It's all off. Lou is not going to buy the play."

"But the contract..."

"All copies still at her lawyers, not signed yet. She's in the clear."

"Bob worked so hard, so long...How could she?"

"You must remember that the lady is allergic to any breath of scandal among her associates. She takes care of the scandal department herself and, at the moment, she's trying hard to keep within the limits of what the box office will bear. The notorious Lou Symington in a movie written by a man suspected of murdering his mistress' husband is a combination a little too gamey even for this broad-minded age. How can you pay Marienberg now?"

"I suppose I can borrow from the bank."

"Second mortgage on the house?"

"It's already mortgaged to the hilt to pay medical bills for Buzz. But I'm sure they'll let me have a loan."

"They might now. They won't after Bob is fired. Loans without collateral depend on earning capacity."

"How long do I have?"

"A few hours."

"As close as that?"

"It may be too late even now if they've been listening to the radio too. Once they hear that Bob is wanted for questioning, they'll expect him to be fired."

Susan looked at her watch. "It's just halfpast one. If I can get away from the Lieutenant by two — or even two-thirty — I can get to the bank before it closes at three."

"New York bank?"

"Yes, luckily."

"Can you get all the dope you need in half an hour?"

"I have everything in a safe deposit box there. We had a loan that we paid off four years ago, but we kept the records."

"So it's really sort of renewing a loan. That you might be able to do, if Bob's arrest isn't on the air before three o'clock."

"Why should the bank care if he's arrested?"

"Oh, come now, Sue! That's obvious. They'd know at once he'd lose his job."

"Then I'm doing a dishonest thing, asking them for a loan before they know?"

"You'll do a lot of dishonest things before this is over. Remember, you're fighting for Bob's life. And don't weep for the poor, dear bank. If you can't pay it, they'll get the money out of your house or your other assets somehow . . . Sue."

Dorfmann waited until he had her full attention. "Do you think it's possible that Bob killed this man?"

"I know he didn't. Bob couldn't do a thing like that."

Susan checked herself as the door opened.

The Lieutenant entered briskly. "Easy enough to pinpoint the restaurant. Girl at the reception desk heard them talking a few days ago about their favorite luncheon place — only place in New York where you can get real scampi flown in from the Adriatic. That's Burano's. I've sent a man there with instructions to contact me here if either of them show, but I don't expect them to now."

"Why not?"

"Those damn news hounds." Casovitz stuck a limp cigarette in one corner of his mouth. "The first spot news was on the air at one o'clock, radio and TV both. Novacz murdered, Robert Lundy wanted for questioning." He struck a match, lifted it towards his mouth. "Kyra Novacz is on a plane to the Argentine by this time and Robert Lundy is with her."

"I'm not. I'm right here."

At the sound of Bob's voice, Casovitz' hand was arrested in mid-air. Susan's head jerked around like a puppet's on a string pulled by an unskilled hand.

Bob stood in the doorway. He had just come in from outside. The hat in his hand scattered raindrops on the floor, his overcoat was soaked. His eyes were red-rimmed and blood-shot, his face scored with deep lines and mottled with uneven color. He had never looked worse and Susan had never loved him more.

"Oh, Bob!" She ran into his arms. Both Dorfmann and Casovitz looked their astonishment. Susan realized she was not playing the part of a deceived wife according to established precedent. Bob was no more convincing in the role of errant husband. He kissed her and kept one arm around her as he turned to look at the other two men. "Quite a little reception you arranged for me, Dorf."

"I couldn't help it." Dorfmann sighed.

Casovitz was a hunter who believed in the quick pounce for the kill. "Where have you been, Mr. Lundy? We've traced your movements until you left the hotel with Mrs. Novacz this morning around ten o'clock. Where did you go then?"

"We parted company at the subway station at 33rd," said Bob. "She was going to take a train to Grand Central and then a shuttle to the West Side subway. She was going to meet her husband, who was due from Washington around ten o'clock."

"Was it her intention to ask him for a divorce, so she could marry you?"

Bob's eyes sought Susan's, mutely pleading.

What does he want? thought Susan. *Oh, what does he want me to say?*

"No." Bob achieved a choking parody of a laugh. "Come, Lieutenant. You're a policeman so you must have had considerable experience of life. A man doesn't marry every woman he makes a pass at. I never had the slightest intention of marrying Kyra Novacz. I love my wife and children. I don't want another family. I have a family."

Now Susan thought she understood. He's lying to protect her. He thinks she's guilty because he knows he's innocent himself. If he can make them believe this lie of his, she won't be arrested because, as the Lieutenant said, you cannot convince a jury without establishing a motive.

"Where is Mrs. Novacz now?" demanded Casovitz.

"I have no idea."

"When did you last see her?"

"I just told you — at the 33rd Street subway station a little after ten. She went down the steps into the subway. I was going to walk to my office."

"But you didn't. Where did you go?"

"I'm afraid you won't believe me when I say I just walked in the rain."

"From ten o'clock to one-thirty? You're right. I don't believe you."

"I had a lot to think about."

"Such as what?"

"And I wasted a lot of time looking for a taxi in the rain."

Dorfmann intervened. "Bob, don't say anything more until you've talked to a lawyer. Susan and I are going to get Marienberg."

"Why? I have nothing to hide," said Bob. "I didn't do it."

"But you have to prove you didn't do it. That's why you need Marienberg."

The Lieutenant moved between them. "Lundy, you're coming over to Homicide West with me for further questioning. You can call your lawyer from there."

"Why can't he call his lawyer right now from this office?" demanded Dorfmann. "Then Marienberg can meet you both at Homicide West when you get there."

The Lieutenant's eyes measured Dorfmann for a moment — not Dorfmann as a man, but Dorfmann as a power in the world.

"Okay." He turned to Bob reluctantly. "You call Marienberg and then we'll go."

Dorfmann was asking the girl on the switchboard for an outside line, when there came a knock on the door.

"Go away, whoever you are. We're busy!" shouted Dorfmann.

But the door opened. A man who seemed like a younger, softer edition of Casovitz stepped just inside the room and held the door open for a woman.

"She was there waiting for him," said the man. "Thought you'd still be here, so I brought her right over in a taxi."

And there was Kyra. Hatless, raindrops on the short, straight, drab hair. School-girlish in her shabby, shapeless, wool coat without any fur. Rain, or tears, had washed powder from her nose, and it was a little red and shiny. Her lipstick was a pale shade, almost the natural color of her lips. Her mouth was expressionless. It might have been carved from pink stone. Her eyes were very wide, as she looked at Bob, and her voice was very small and childish, when she spoke to him, almost lisping.

"Oh, Bob! How could you? How could you kill poor, old, darling Dada? You knew I loved him!"

The tears sprang and rolled down her cheeks. The young man, who had brought her there, was moved to pat her on the shoulder. "It's all right, Mrs. Novacz. He won't get away with it!"

CHAPTER ELEVEN

ON THE COMMUTERS' TRAIN that took Susan back to Westchester, two Abingdon men sat in the seat behind her. Both had read the evening paper.

"This Lundy fellow, did you ever meet him?" said one.

"I've been trying to remember, but I don't believe I ever did," said the other. "Boy, has he got himself into a sweet mess!"

"There, but for the grace of God ..." returned the first man. "Two years ago I had a secretary ... well ..."

Both laughed. The first one went on: "Do you remember that story of Tolstoi's, *The Death of Ivan Ilyitch?* Each person, who heard Ivan was dead, had the same reaction: *Thank God, it wasn't I!* That was the reaction in the bar car tonight when I passed through it."

"Fellow must be a bit of a fool. You just don't go off the deep end after every roll in the hay."

"That's easy to say, but you never know when one of these little bitches will get under your skin and make a damned fool of you."

"Yeah, it's like liquor. You think you can handle it and then, sometimes, you can't."

The train was slowing down for Abingdon station. Susan rose and made her way unsteadily towards the door, legs braced against the swaying of the car. She was the first to step down into the snow and darkness. By the dusty glare of station lamps, she picked her way towards the taxi stand.

"Where to, lady?" Happily he was not one of the drivers who knew her by sight.

"Toilsome Hill Lane."

"Let's wait a bit and see if there are any others going that way."

Susan sat in the far corner of the back seat, grateful for the darkness. Two men got into the cab. One sat beside Susan, one beside the driver. Both were strangers and both carried evening papers. Susan glanced at the front page of the *New York Star*, tabloid in spirit, though not in format.

There were pictures. Bob, standing between two policemen, in front of the courthouse, where he had been arraigned. Robin's class at school, with an arrow pointing to Robin in the second row. They must have got that from one of Robin's classmates. A wedding picture of Bob and herself, and one of Bob in uniform when he won his citation. Those had probably come out of the newspaper morgue. There were no pictures of Kyra or Novacz, but there was one of the apartment house on Riverside Drive, with another arrow pointing to the windows of the Novacz' apartment.

As the taxi lurched into motion, the driver said to the two men: "Toilsome Hill Lane first."

"Say!" cried the man who shared the back seat with Susan. "Isn't that where the Lundys live?"

"Could be," returned the driver. "It didn't say on the radio. Just Abingdon, New York."

Susan thanked God for the small blessing.

"Wonder which house is theirs?"

Both men peered into the darkness.

"Probably no one there now. If I were in a mess like that, I wouldn't stay in a small town. I'd head for the city, where you can get lost."

Susan felt as if she were naked. Yet this was only a foretaste of what life in Abingdon was going to be like during the next few months. The vulture press would peel clothing, and then skin, from her private life, and Bob's. What would all this do to Robin and Buzz?

The taxi stopped. She counted out the exact change with trembling fingers and added a good tip. "Good night!" cried the driver. "Good night!" chorussed the other passengers. How much longer would she hear that note of friendly respect in any Abingdon voices? How strange it was to think that the tone would have been one of avid and prurient curiosity tonight, if they had known who she was . . .

She stood still for a moment, one hand on a gatepost, using the moment of solitude as a breathing space to gather her strength together before she entered the house and faced the children. There were lights at all the windows. The house made her think of a lighted ship, battling its way through perilous seas in darkness. Dear little barque, it had weathered other storms, but none like this. And now . . . *don't weep for the poor, dear bank. They'll get the money out of your house or something* . . . Was she going to lose her home physically as well as spiritually?

Her gaze took in familiar details, masked by snow, dim by

starlight. The open terrace, where they used to have lobster suppers in summer. The herb garden, where she had planted so much mint and thyme. The lilac bush, the rose bushes, the wisteria vine. The lawn that sloped down to the muddy brook where the weeping willows grew. The front door and shutters that Bob had painted himself in a pale blue the year that they couldn't afford a painter because polio is an expensive disease.

A happy home. As Kyra had said. Her hand tightened into a fist and struck the gatepost with all her force. This was what she was fighting for and, for this, she would do anything.

She walked up the driveway. There was a station wagon parked on the grass verge between the driveway and the road, but she was too preoccupied to wonder about it. The front door was usually locked when the children were alone after dark, but this time her key wouldn't turn. It was several moments before she understood that the door was unlocked. She pushed it open.

"Mommy!" Robin came tearing out of the living room and threw herself into Susan's arms. How unlike the reserved, almost hostile teen-ager of this morning! Susan held her close and kissed her. She returned the kiss as she used to before she became self-conscious about kissing anybody.

"Where's Buzz?" He couldn't run because of the braces.

"In the living room with Mrs. Trumbull."

"Kate Trumbull?"

"Yes. She came over to be with us as soon as she heard the radio at one o'clock. She was here when we got home from school. We didn't know anything until she told us."

Susan's eyes stung with tears. In this new world she was living in now, any act of disinterested kindness came as a surprise, not at all what she expected of fellow human beings. She still had her arm around Robin's waist as they walked to-

gether into the living room. Kate Trumbull had made a fire
and it was blazing cheerfully. She must have dressed hastily,
as soon as she heard the broadcast. Her lipstick was crooked,
her shirt the wrong color for her slacks, but, to Susan, she
looked perfectly beautiful.

"I don't know how to thank you, Kate."

"I'm so glad I happened to have the radio on when I did,
but you keep it on most of the time when you're living alone.
Otherwise the silence gets on your nerves. I've started supper
and there are things I must do in the kitchen now. But let me
get you a drink first."

For the first time Susan summoned the courage to look at
Buzz. He had the same stricken look she saw in Robin's eyes,
but there was something else besides. Perhaps it was just his
masculinity that made him look more stormy and accusing
than Robin.

"Hi, mom!" He was less demonstrative, too.

Kate came back from the kitchen with a pitcher of Martinis,
poured one for Susan and one for herself. "Now I shall be busy
in the kitchen for the next ten minutes. Please don't bother
me! I'm an amateur cook, you know, and I have to concen-
trate!"

Did the children see through Kate's subterfuge for leaving
the three of them alone together for a little while, but not too
long?

Susan sat down on the sofa. The Martini glass was too full.
She took a sip and then set it down on the coffee table carefully, so it wouldn't spill. She really didn't feel like a drink
just then.

Robin sat close beside her, gazing up into her face. Buzz
stood facing her.

"He didn't do it, mommy, did he?" cried Robin.

"Of course he didn't. You know your father is incapable of

murder. We'll have a rough time for the next few weeks, proving that to other people, but we'll do it. He'll be free in no time."

Buzz said: "Are you sure he didn't do it?"

Susan rose and put her hands on the boy's shoulders. "I am absolutely sure, Buzz. And you must be absolutely sure, too. If you love people, you have faith in them."

But Buzz was not comforted. His eyes stared up into hers. "Is the rest of it true? About that Kyra woman?"

Susan could not meet his eyes. She used her drink as an excuse to turn away and picked it up. That gave her a moment for reflection. It was too late for lies. You couldn't go on denying what might be in every newspaper for weeks or months to come.

"Yes, Buzz. That part is true. If it were not, they wouldn't have suspected him of killing Kyra's husband."

"And did Daddy ask you for a divorce?"

"Yes."

"Was he going to leave us for good?"

A cry broke from Robin. "Oh, don't! Oh, please don't get a divorce!" She buried her face on her mother's shoulder, sobbing.

Susan sat like a stone. To the very end of her life, she would never forget that dying fall in Robin's voice.

Buzz spoke in the coldest voice she had ever heard. "A man like Daddy shouldn't marry and have children."

Robin was wounded to the heart. Buzz was angry. To a daughter, the father was the more important parent. Robin cared more than Buzz, but she couldn't blame her father for anything. To a son, the mother was the more important parent. So, mingled with Buzzy's grief, was resentment and anger at Bob for hurting Buzzy's mother.

"Maybe it's our fault!" cried Robin. "Buzzy's and mine. If

we hadn't been so bratty, maybe Daddy wouldn't —"

"No, Robin. That's not true and Daddy himself would be the first to tell you so. Buzz, please try to understand. You're old enough now. All men are like your father. You'll be like him some day."

"All men don't get divorces."

"No, but all men are at the mercy of unscrupulous women." How Bob would hate the suggestion that Kyra was in any way to blame. She must not use the children to feed her hatred of Kyra. So, with a great effort, she said: "And it isn't always the fault of the woman. Sometimes she, too, is carried away against her will and regrets everything as much as the man does."

"But nice women don't do such things, do they?" said Robin.

"No." After all she could not let Robin grow to womanhood believing that Kyra's conduct had been wholly admirable. "Let's put it this way: a nice woman, the kind of woman you'll be, never puts herself in a situation where she can be carried away against her will. There is always a time, at the beginning of any love affair, when you can stop it, if you will. But if you don't stop then, if you let it go on, thinking you can remain in control of it, you may find you cannot, when it is too late. The nice woman is the woman who stops while there is still time."

Robin wasn't listening. "Oh, mommy! We need him. And he doesn't need us! That's so awful!"

"I don't need him," said Buzz, bitterly.

Everything was getting out of hand. Susan must pull them in another direction, away from bitterness. Shock and grief and fear were bad enough, but there must not be bitterness. That would destroy them.

"Buzz, Robin — listen to me. I have no question in my mind that Daddy loves all three of us It's one thing to love people.

It's something else to be in love with somebody. When a man loves his family and then falls in love with another woman, he's torn in two and suffers more than anyone else involved."

"Why is 'in love' different?" asked Robin, lifting swollen eyes.

"You're both old enough to understand the difference between love that is based on shared memories, and love that is based on a sexual impulse."

"But it isn't just a sexual impulse," said Buzz. "He wants to marry her."

"He didn't in the beginning. And it doesn't mean that he loves us less just because he now loves her more than he did in the beginning."

I sound like Pollyanna. But what else can I say? They must not lose their faith in their father's love at this age. That's the road to the psychiatrist's couch . . .

"I suppose you really are too young to understand, but you must try, for my sake, as well as Daddy's. No matter what happens, don't doubt his love for you, or for me. True love does not die."

Buzz looked skeptical, but Robin was interested. "Mother, at school girls often have crushes on boys and get over them in a few weeks. That's not true love, is it?"

"No."

"Well, isn't it possible that this is something Daddy might get over some day?"

How easy, how self-comforting to say yes, but how dangerous to raise a false hope. She picked her way among her words as delicately as if she were walking among land mines. "It is always possible, Robin, because in this world, anything is possible, and the future is always unpredictable. I don't believe the expected ever happens. But when things have gone as far as this, it's most unlikely that Daddy will get over it.

What we must do now is to fix firmly in our minds the idea that, no matter what he does, he loves us. He would say the same thing, if he were here, I'm sure."

"Would you take him back, if he wanted to come back?" asked Robin.

Susan hesitated. Her own thoughts had not ranged so far afield.

"Oh, mommy, you would, wouldn't you?"

Susan kissed Robin. "Of course. I love him. How could I not love your father?" But in her heart, Susan wondered. . . . Am I misleading them? Could I take him back? Wouldn't it depend on his reasons for wanting to come back?

Buzz had not relaxed his grimness, but now he spoke more briskly. "Well, we'll just have to make the best of it."

To Susan, there was something pathetic about that artificial briskness. She drew him into her arms and he came stiffly, awkwardly, almost resisting her. "The important thing now isn't really whether Daddy loves us or not, but whether we love him or not. We can control our own feelings, though we can't control his. Love isn't something you take. It's something you give. Daddy is in great trouble and danger. He has been accused of murder. We know he's innocent and we must do everything we can to help him prove it."

"How can we?" cried Robin.

"I've got a lawyer. I'm seeing him in New York tomorrow. You can help me by being strong and not minding if I don't stay with you as much as I'd like to at this time."

Buzz was struck by a sudden thought. "Are we going to school tomorrow?"

"Dinner is served, madam," said Kate from the dining room doorway.

"You're pretty formal," said Buzz. "Robin just yells 'Come and get it or I'll give it to the dogs!' "

"Do you know what my little son used to say when he fed his puppies?" said Kate. "He'd call out: 'Come and get it or I'll give it to the people!'"

Buzz thought this very funny. Robin looked as if she didn't think anything would ever be funny again. She didn't pick up her fork. After a few minutes, Buzz put his down. He wasn't quite as tough as he was pretending.

"What these children need is a good sleep," said Kate.

To Susan's surprise, Buzz turned to her almost pleading. "Mommy, could I have one of those pills I had when I was sick?"

"If there's one left, yes." Susan went upstairs, to the medicine cabinet. There were two sleeping pills left. She brought them downstairs. "Here, Buzz." She handed him one, with a glass of water.

"Thanks."

Susan watched him swallow, remembering how he had hated those pills when he was in physical pain, how she and Bob had to cajole him into taking one.

"Good night, Mrs. Trumbull." Susan and Robin went upstairs with Buzz; Robin helped him take off his braces, tucked him in. He put his arms around Susan's neck as she bent to kiss him. "Oh, mommy!" She just held him. There was nothing more she could say. He spoke drowsily, as the pill began to work. "Will you leave the night light on?"

"Of course, Buzz." He hadn't had a night light for over a year now, but she left it on. She and Robin tiptoed out of the room, and went down the stairs together.

"Aren't you ready for sleep, Robin?"

"I couldn't sleep."

"There's another pill. Would you like it?"

"Save it for Buzz."

"I can get more tomorrow."

"I don't want to sleep. I want to think."

"Then have some supper."

"I can't eat."

"Leave her alone," said Kate. "It never hurt a healthy child to miss one meal, but it can hurt her to eat, if she isn't hungry."

"What about school tomorrow?" said Robin. "You never answered Buzz when he asked you."

"I couldn't think of an answer," said Susan.

"I have an idea about that," said Kate. "Isn't your Christmas vacation starting in about two weeks?"

"Yes."

"Well, if your mother will let you, why don't you and Buzz come and stay with me over at Hilltop? You can just skip school for those last two weeks."

"But there are exams."

"You can arrange to take them later, I'm sure. I'd love to have you with me. It's lonely at my house now. Your mother will have to be in New York a lot the next few weeks. She'll be easier in her mind, if you're not here alone with Buzz, and you can help me paint the fence and mow the lawn and all kinds of things."

"Wouldn't that be running away?" said Robin.

"What's the matter with running away?" retorted Kate. "Soldiers do it all the time. They call it 'executing a strategic movement to the rear.' They know 'he who fights and runs away will live to fight another day.' Why should civilians be braver than soldiers and stick where they are, even if it means defeat? Sometimes you have to lose a battle in order to win a war. It's the war that counts, not the battle, and this going to school for two weeks or not, isn't even a battle. Just a skirmish."

"How right you are, Kate," said Susan. "I don't know what

I would have done, if you hadn't been here tonight. I don't seem to be able to think clearly any more."

"Of course you can't now. You're the one who really needs a good night's rest. You'd better take that second pill yourself. Robin, you'd better be off to bed now. We'll all be up early and drive your mother to the station, and then we'll go to my house."

"Good night, mother." Robin kissed Susan with the real tenderness that is so rare in a teen-ager.

"Darling, the most helpful thing you can do right now is to get a good night's sleep. If you change your mind about that pill, let me know."

When Robin had gone, the two women took coffee into the living room.

Kate had been reading the newspaper that was delivered to the house every evening. Now she looked at Susan directly. "Do you think Bob is guilty?"

"No."

"Then surely a good lawyer like Marienberg can get him off?"

"I hope so."

"The only other person with an obvious motive is Kyra Novacz herself. Why didn't the police arrest her?"

"I don't know. Maybe she has an alibi and Bob doesn't."

"You'd better get Marienberg to find out, if he can. And, Susan, don't you think you'd better prepare your mind, and the children's, for the possibility that Bob is guilty?"

"I know he didn't do it," said Susan, fiercely.

"Would you still say that, if he were convicted?"

"Of course. But he won't be convicted. He can't be."

"You'd better take your pill and go to bed."

Susan had risen, when Robin came back into the living

room in pink, padded robe and fluffy, pink slippers. She carried a little, red, leather book in one hand. Her eyes were
quick with excitement.

"Mother! I've just thought of something. This afternoon,
after school, Mrs. Trumbull told us to clean up the guest
room for you, strip the bed and empty the scrapbasket and
all that."

Two birds with one stone, thought Susan. Occupational
therapy for the children and a way to remove every trace of
Kyra before I got home.

"When we were doing it, I found this little address book.
Kyra Novacz must have left it here. Maybe there could be
some clue in it, because if Daddy didn't murder her husband,
she must be the one."

Susan almost laughed. It was incongruous, treating a tragedy
in real life as if it were an artificial, cops-and-robbers comedy
on the TV screen.

But she answered Robin gently. "I can't see how we could
get any clues out of an address book."

"But, mother! At the very least, it would tell us about other
people she knew. Maybe there are other men in her life. Maybe
one of them killed her husband."

Kate was looking at Susan oddly. "The child's right, Sue. It
might give Marienberg some sort of line on Kyra's associates.
You know so little about her, really. Give the thing to Marienberg and see if he can make anything out of it."

When Robin had gone back to bed, Kate added: "You
shouldn't dampen her enthusiasm like that. It would do her
good to feel that she was helping."

"But it's so melodramatic, Kate." Susan dropped the little
book on the coffee table. "People don't leave address books
around if there are important secrets in them."

"If you're not curious, I am." Kate picked up the book and began to leaf through it with absorption.

After a few moments, Susan felt her own curiosity stir. "Well? Any messages in cipher?"

"No, but there's one thing that distinguishes three of the entries from all the others."

"And that is?"

"All but these three are entered alphabetically, under the initial letter of the surname, and the name is given in full, with address and telephone number. But these three entries are on the flyleaf, with no names or addresses at all, just Manhattan telephone numbers. These must be entries she wanted to hide from somebody — her husband, I suppose. It might be worth Marienberg's while to find out whose numbers these are."

Susan leaned over Kate's shoulder. It was the first time she had seen Kyra's handwriting. It was like her voice — small, faint, thin, without character or emphasis.

"I know one of those numbers," said Susan. "It's Bob's office number."

"And the other two?"

"I have no idea, and yet — it's funny. I have a feeling I've seen at least one of them. It must be a number of someone we know."

CHAPTER TWELVE

SUSAN WAS KEPT WAITING in a reception room at Mr. Marienberg's office for some time that next morning. She had smoked six cigarettes and leafed twice through a three-months-old copy of *Life*, until she could endure sitting still no longer. She was alone in the room, so she felt free to walk about, examining the pictures on the wall with open curiosity.

It was then that she discovered they were all pictures of Marienberg himself. Photographs of him addressing meetings, caricatures of him by several famous cartoonists, a carefully posed studio portrait by a well known photographer of men, and, finally, a framed letter from a retired judge of the State Supreme Court, saying what an excellent lawyer he was. She felt she had learned quite a lot about his appearance and character before the receptionist opened the door and announced that Mr. Marienberg would see her now.

He looked more like the caricatures than the photographs, as he rose and leaned across his massive desk to shake hands. His hair was dark, but his eyes were a bleak blue. She had never seen colder eyes. The chin, that gave such opportunity to cartoonists, was thrust forward, like a chip on the shoulder, as if he were daring everyone to sock him on the jaw. The name had sounded Semitic to her, but, now she saw him, she was sure it was Teutonic. Many Jews have many faults, but coldness is not one of them.

As she sat down, Susan realized that all this was very bad indeed. She had taken a dislike to the man even before he opened his mouth. She tried to tell herself that she needed his egoism and truculence. They were on her side, and Bob's, to be used as weapons against the prosecution. But she could not make herself believe this after Marienberg had talked to her for a few minutes.

"Mrs. Lundy, I am advising your husband to plead guilty. That way he should get off with a prison sentence, since this murder was obviously unpremeditated. If he gets time off for good conduct in prison, he will only be away for a few years."

"But he didn't do it!" cried Susan.

"Can you prove that?"

"No, but —"

"What you cannot prove is useless in court. From the legal point of view, the case against him could not be blacker. He had every motive in the world, as you know. He had no witnesses to his story of how he spent his time during those crucial hours from ten to one-thirty on the day of the crime."

"Doesn't all this apply to Mrs. Novacz as well?"

"If the police thought so, they would have arrested her. The fact that she has not even been charged as an accessory, suggests that she must have an abili well supported by several witnesses. Novacz was a diabetic. It would have been so easy for his wife to kill him by insulin shock. All she had to do was withhold the insulin. How could the police ever have proved that that was not accident? But Novacz was killed with one blow that could not possibly have been accident or suicide."

"One blow?" repeated Susan. "The murderer must be a strong man."

"Not necessarily. Novacz had a paperweight on his desk, shaped like a miniature anvil. It must have been made before the turn of the century, when toys like that were well made, for it was an exact replica of a real anvil in miniature, and it was made of heavy iron, not plastic or aluminum. It weighed several pounds. Like all anvils, one end was pointed quite sharply. Apparently, the murderer held it by the base and swung it once at Novacz' temple, where the skull bone is thinnest. The weight and sharpness combined made a perfect weapon and it crashed through the bone, penetrating the brain to a depth of an inch and a half. With a heavy weapon like that, you do not need strength. A child can wield a hammer effectively, using the weight of the hammer itself in place of strength. But this weapon was more deadly than a hammer, because it was pointed, as well as heavy. That point caught inside the broken bone. The murderer left it there and it was there when the police found it."

"Why would he leave it?" demanded Susan.

"Why not? There was nothing about the weapon that would identify the murderer. It belonged to Novacz, and leaving it in the wound staunched the flow of blood. It's when you withdraw a piercing weapon that blood flows and splatters. There wasn't much blood in this case. I doubt if the murderer was spattered at all. It would be chance if he were."

"So the murder was unpremeditated?"

"A calculating murderer would probably have used the

insulin shock method. So much safer. But someone lost control, in a rage, beside himself, and grasped the nearest object at hand and struck . . . maybe not even with intent to kill. And then when he saw what he had done he fled leaving the weapon where it was."

"Fingerprints?"

"None. But in December weather like this everyone wears gloves."

"You don't know Kyra has an alibi. You're just guessing."

"We can't know the details until the case comes into court, but I am certain that, if any case could be made out against her at all, she would have been charged at the same time as your husband."

"And he has no alibi?"

"None whatever. Mr. Lundy has modified his first impulsive statement to the police because I advised him to do so. He now admits that he wanted to marry Mrs. Novacz and that he had already asked you for a divorce. He also admits that he did not know Mrs. Novacz had a husband until the Friday before the crime and the discovery was a great shock to him. He has to admit this in order to make his story of how he spent those crucial three and a half hours at all credible, and it still isn't credible enough. We're trying hard to find some witness who remembers seeing him at that time, but I've just about given up hope that we will."

"Has Bob agreed to plead guilty?"

"No. I was hoping you might persuade him to do so."

"What is his story of the three and a half hours now?"

"He says that he and Mrs. Novacz walked to the East Side subway station on 33rd Street together and parted there some time after ten. They walked slowly because they were talking. She was going to take a shuttle at Grand Central to the West

Side subway and walk from a West Side subway station to her apartment on Riverside Drive, where she expected to meet her husband, due back from Washington at ten, and ask him for a divorce. Bob Lundy says he wanted to go with her to protect her from her husband's anger, but she insisted it would be better if she saw her husband alone. Lundy agreed, reluctantly. He told her he would go to his office and wait for her to telephone him there as soon as the interview with her husband was over."

"But he didn't. Why not?"

"He claims that he started walking towards his office and then, after walking about twenty minutes, he decided he just couldn't stand the thought of her facing her husband alone. It seems that Novacz had peasant ideas about striking his wife. So Lundy stood on a street corner, trying to hail a taxi. That is supposed to account for another thirty minutes. At that time he intended to follow her to her husband's apartment in a taxi and be present during the interview. At least, that's what Bob says now.

"You will recall that it was raining hard and we all know how difficult it is to get an unoccupied taxi on a rainy day in Manhattan. Pure luck, if you do, and Bob Lundy had no luck that morning.

"He says that around eleven-thirty he decided that his best bet would be Grand Central Station, where there are always taxis going in and out with railway passengers. He used up another twenty minutes walking to the station — or so he says. That would make it about eleven-forty when he reached the taxi stand at Grand Central. He insists that he wasted a lot of time there at the taxi stand. Unfortunately, though a dispatcher was on duty, and a policeman was directing traffic there, because of the rain, neither one remembers seeing him.

"He says there was a line of people ahead of him and, after a few minutes, a train from Chicago came in and discharged passengers. Because they had luggage, the dispatcher gave them preference. Lundy says he and several others protested this was unfair, and the dispatcher said if they didn't like it, they could look for taxis elsewhere. The dispatcher remembers this altercation, but not Bob Lundy.

"He says that he went to a restaurant in the station — Cobb's Corner — and spent 'quite a while' (whatever that means) drinking coffee and waiting until the Chicago passengers were gone. He was sure he could get a taxi then, and finally did — only to find that particular taxi wouldn't start. The battery was dead. He moved towards another taxi and a woman in a purple hat pushed her way past him and got it. He couldn't have stopped her, short of physical violence.

"Exasperated, he looked at his watch. To his amazement, he found it was nearly one o'clock. He had spent far more time on this taxi business than he had any idea. He explains this lack of time-sense by saying that his worry about Kyra had left him in a highly emotional mood — a mood of indecision, and confusion."

"It may be true," cried Susan. "He did forget that he and Dorfmann had an important appointment with someone at Tantamount that morning."

"He also says that once you have spent a certain amount of time waiting for a taxi you hate to give up. You feel that the time already spent will be wasted unless you stick it out. It's like supporting a business financially because you've already invested in it. Once you've invested an hour waiting for a taxi, you'll invest another twenty minutes so as not to lose the hour altogether."

"That's true," said Susan. "I always think that if I wait just one more minute, an empty taxi is sure to come along."

"Sometimes one has to give up. Bob Lundy says he gave up at five to one. He was appalled at the thought that Kyra might have telephoned him at his office already when he was not there, as he had told her he would be. She might need him desperately and not know where to find him. So he walked as rapidly as possible to his office from Grand Central. That walk used up the last thirty minutes. When he reached the office at one-thirty, he was informed by the receptionist that Daniel Novacz had been murdered, that the police were looking for him, Bob Lundy, and that one of them was already in Mr. Dorfmann's office, interviewing you. Naturally he went straight to Dorfmann's office and you know the rest."

"All this could be the truth!" insisted Susan.

"It could, but . . . there are no witnesses and three and a half hours is an awfully long time to look for a taxi even in New York on a rainy day. That's why I want you to urge him to plead guilty."

"I can't do that. I want him acquitted."

Marienberg sighed audibly. "You're making a mistake."

"I'll take that responsibility." Susan had a feeling that her opposition to Marienberg's ideas was doubly unpalatable to him because she was a woman. She was sure now of some Teutonic element in his background. His unsmiling face said so eloquently that women should do as they were told, especially when they were told by Lee Marienberg.

"How did Kyra Novacz learn about the murder that morning? Did the policeman who brought her to Dorfmann's office tell her? She already knew all about it when she walked into the office and said: 'Oh, Bob, how could you?' "

"The radio was turned on in the taxi a young policeman used to bring her to Dorfmann's office from Burano's restaurant. From a broadcast she learned that Novacz had been murdered and that Bob had no alibi. He was missing. The police wanted him for questioning. So, the moment she saw him in Dorfmann's office, she threw him to the wolves in order to save herself from the charge of accessory. *Oh, Bob, how could you when you knew I loved Dada* or whatever it was. Lieutenant Casovitz was annoyed, naturally. He had wanted to break the news to her and catch her reaction. But the young policeman was new to this work and he goofed."

"Maybe the murder wasn't news to her."

"You do think she killed Novacz?"

"Perhaps she found his body at the apartment before she went to the restaurant and didn't report it to the police because she was afraid of being accused of the murder. Perhaps Novacz' death was the 'bad news' she said she had for Bob when she telephoned him and I took the call."

"She says the bad news was Novacz' refusal to divorce her," said Marienberg. "Obviously, if Bob did go to Novacz' apartment after Kyra left, Novacz would have said the same thing to Bob. So it is really Kyra's testimony that establishes his motive."

"They have no evidence against Bob except his motive and his weak alibi."

"We have no way of knowing what evidence they have. But they wouldn't charge Bob unless they had something more — either something that implicates him more deeply or something that clears Kyra, the only other suspect with a motive."

"I know Bob is innocent. There must be some way to prove the truth."

"Not always. Not in court. And now, Mrs. Lundy, I'd like to go over the statement you made to the police. You saw Mrs. Novacz that morning on Riverside Drive?"

Susan went through the tale of her encounter with Kyra for the second time.

"And then she left you?"

"She ran away from me, towards the apartment, crying loudly . . ."

"Crying what? Any words?"

Susan was conscious of the responsibility any witness takes who repeats words uttered in haste, in a highly emotional state, without perhaps a full sense of their meaning. *But what else can I do? I have to tell him, for Bob's sake* . . .

"I had told her that Novacz told me he would never divorce her. She cried: 'He must! I'll kill him, if he doesn't! I'll kill him!' "

"It's unfortunate that you were the only person to hear those words."

"Why?"

"You're Bob Lundy's wife. He's the father of your children and you are standing by him publicly, so you must love him. You have good reason to hate Kyra Novacz. The prosecution will suggest that you made up the whole thing, in order to save Bob. And so will Kyra, if she gets a chance on the witness stand."

Susan searched her mind desperately for something in Bob's favor. "There are no witnesses who put Bob in the neighborhood of the Novacz' apartment at the crucial time, are there?"

"I live in fear that one will turn up at the trial as a witness for the prosecution."

"Wouldn't they have to have such testimony in order to convict Bob?"

"Theoretically, yes, but in practice — don't be too sure of that."

"Are you serious?"

"My dear Mrs. Lundy, all verdicts are actually based upon assumptions and probabilities, not proof, though we lawyers hate to admit it. Of course the police can't prove Bob Lundy killed Daniel Novacz. They're not even supposed to prove it. Who ever proved anything, in, or out, of court? We simply presume things on the basis of probability, which, in the hands of a skillful advocate is usually just plausibility. Like magicians, we lawyers make our points through misdirection. We heighten what we want the jury to notice and glide past the things we don't want them to notice. Proof beyond a reasonable doubt, we say. And what, pray, is a reasonable doubt? Can anyone, even a lawyer, define that? What's an unreasonable doubt?

"Someone killed Novacz. The police know of two people with motives. They think they can make — observe that word 'make' — a better case against one, your husband, than the other, Mrs. Novacz. So they charge your husband, for, a prosecutor automatically looks for the person who will be easiest to convict, rather than the person most likely to be guilty.

"A jury is deeply affected by the emotional tone of a case, which has nothing to do with proof. The prosecution will present your husband to the jury with the greatest cunning as an unsympathetic character, a husband and father, who is leaving his family for another woman, and this will affect the verdict profoundly, because unconsciously.

"Analyze almost any old court record and you will find that nothing was proved — only certain assumptions were made. That's what makes a court room scene dramatic. Even at the end, when the verdict is in and sentence is pronounced, we know that we still don't know really whether the verdict is the truth or not. A trial ends, as it begins, with a question mark. A hundred years later, a shrewd jurist can take any historical case apart and put it together again and thus convince you that the losing side should have won.

"Do you expect justice to prevail when you go into a gambling house? Of course not. And when you go into court, you are simply gambling that your side will win. It has nothing to do with whether your side is right or not. Juries cannot weigh one fact against another for they do not have all the facts. All they can do is to weigh one probability against another. The decision depends on chance and mood. Facts are nothing without emotional overtones. In this case, I predict that your husband will be tried for murder and convicted for adultery."

Susan looked into the cold, blue eyes and saw there an absolute certainty of defeat.

He's given up already. And it was to pay this man that I borrowed money from the bank . . .

Outside, a wintry wind was scouring the crosstown streets as she walked to the offices of K., K., D., and V.

"Well?" said Dorfmann.

"It looks pretty bad, Alan. Marienberg doesn't believe in Bob's innocence."

"There are times when I don't either."

"Alan! You can't feel that way."

"Kyra sounded awfully convincing to me when she cried out: 'Oh, Bob, how could you?'"

"She didn't to me."

"After all, who else could have murdered Novacz? It must have been either Bob or Kyra herself. No one else had a motive. It's another case of the lady or the tiger."

"But Bob isn't a tiger. And Kyra isn't a lady."

"Then who do you think murdered Novacz?"

"What can I say? I only know that Bob didn't do it. I had so hoped we might get some lead out of the address book, but

Marienberg was so discouraging, I didn't even bother to show it to him. I don't think he'd pay the slightest attention to it, if I did."

"What address book?"

"Kyra's. She left it at our house. There are three anonymous telephone numbers on the flyleaf. Obviously numbers she didn't want her husband to identify. One of them is Bob's office number."

"Let's see the other two."

Susan handed the book across the desk.

"Well, I'll be damned!" said Dorfmann.

"You know one of them?"

"Sure. So do you probably. You must have seen it in Bob's own address book. It's Don Tishman's number. Our great competitors, Donald Tishman Associates. This is getting interesting."

Dorfmann picked up the telephone, asked for an outside line, and began to dial.

"Mr. Tishman, please . . . Hello, Tish? Alan Dorfmann here . . . I want to talk to you. Can you squeeze me in this morning? . . . Only a couple of minutes . . . You're right. It's about that. I have Mrs. Lundy here in my office and I'm bringing her with me. We'll be right over."

Tishman Associates were on the top floor of another tall, modern palace, mostly glass, as if it had been perversely designed to ensure maximum destruction in the event of nuclear war.

Tishman himself was more like the popular idea of an advertising man than Dorfmann — younger, thinner, taller and dressed with more studied care. A dark suit of rough Italian silk, a fine, white linen shirt, a dull, red tie and narrow shoes that gleamed like black pearls. Pale blond hair had been

brushed flat 'till it clung to his shapely skull, like paint. Beside
him, Dorfmann was dumpy and disheveled, bald and middle-
aged, but the two were obviously friendly enemies.

"Susan, this is Don Tishman."

Obviously he was a man who studied women as intently as
dress. He made a gallant ritual of providing Susan with a chair
and lighting her cigarette.

"You've seen the morning papers?" Dorfmann was abrupt.

"Yes. Bad luck for your firm, Dorf." Tishman looked at
Susan and hesitated, uncertain of protocol at this point. "You
do have all my sympathy, Mrs. Lundy. If there's anything I
can do ..."

"There is," said Dorfmann. "That's why we're here. Your
office phone number, the unlisted one, was in Kyra Novacz'
personal address book. We'd like to know why."

"It's not what you think, Dorf."

"Okay, then, what is it?"

Tishman sat back in his chair, crossing long, handsome legs.
Amusement flickered in his eyes. "You're not going to like this,
Dorf."

"That's not important now. I'll forget it — whatever it is
— if you do what you can to help us get Bob Lundy acquitted. The guy could lose his life, you know."

"I knew Bob, too. And liked him. So, I'll take you at your
word and come clean. Kyra was an employee of ours."

"She told Bob, when he first met her, that she had no job
— just helped Novacz with typing."

"Kyra always was a liar and she had to lie that time."

"Why?"

"She met Bob at the K., K., D., and V. party for Lou
Symington, didn't she?"

"Yeah."

"Well, we sent her there. We wanted to know the kind of line you were going to take with Lou Symington's divorce at that point. You see, we have the Magna Pictures' account and we were handling the publicity on Dick Grant's first wife. We had to be prepared for each move you made."

"Oh . . ." Susan gasped. "She told Bob that she was a gate-crasher, who just wandered in by chance."

"That was better than saying Tishman Associates sent her."

"Bob said then that he had a funny feeling her face was familiar."

"He'd probably seen her once or twice, when he was passing through our offices," answered Tishman.

"Was that her only connection with you?" demanded Dorfmann.

"Yes." Tishman was serious now. "I swear there was nothing else. She was just a sort of freelance spy for us, paid by the job, not on salary. I got an impression her husband didn't know anything about the job and wouldn't have approved, if he had. Also, she might have got into trouble with the immigration authorities, if she didn't watch her step. Her visa, or whatever you call it, probably didn't cover employment in the United States. Her business with us was all very hush-hush."

"And I bet she didn't pay income tax either."

"Maybe. She did ask us to pay her in cash."

"What about your books?"

"We can always squeeze a little cash out of the business expense item listed as *Postage, Paper and Office Supplies.*"

"And that's all? You don't recognize this third phone number?"

"No, I don't. Sorry I can't be more helpful. I suppose you were hoping to find another man in her life?"

"Of course. That might get Bob off the hook . . . if anything can now. At least, it would give someone else a motive for murdering Novacz."

"There was another man I saw her with once," said Tishman. "At the Champagne Room one night. He was an actor, but I can't think of his name."

"Try."

"Rochester? Peekskill?"

"Those are towns, not people."

"Well, he had a name like a town. Some town upstate. Poughkeepsie? No . . . I've got it! Albany. Conrad Albany."

In the windy street again, Dorfmann put Susan into a cab. "Now you go straight back to Marienberg's office and dump this in his lap. Make the guy work for his keep." Dorfmann turned to the driver and gave him Marienberg's address.

"Thank you, Alan . . ."

Dorfmann waved goodbye from the curb as the cab pulled out into traffic.

Make the guy work for his keep . . . But Marienberg wouldn't work. Not on this case. He was just going through the motions of defending Bob. He believed that Bob was guilty. And this slender lead might be Bob's last chance. It should be followed up by someone with faith in Bob, not by a man who would follow it up languidly, or perhaps not even bother to follow it up at all.

Susan asked the driver to stop and wait for her in front of a drug store. She went into the public telephone booth and looked in the Manhattan book under *Albany*. She came out with her chin set at a stubborn angle.

"You'll have to turn around now," she told the driver. "We're going uptown, to the East Seventies."

The Albany telephone number was the third one in Kyra's book.

CHAPTER THIRTEEN

THE HOUSE WAS not at all like the usual New York residence. Susan had that impression the moment she saw it. For one thing, the street was wider than most crosstown streets, and this last house at its eastern end was surrounded by open space on three sides. The street in front, a big, open yard in back, and the river view to the east. Susan knew that at least one of the other houses in the row was divided into cold-water flats. She and Bob had known an artist occupying one of the flats, who heated his own water on an oil stove and lived a countryman's life in the heart of the city.

No doubt the other buildings were the same, yet she had no feeling of being in a slum. You didn't think of a slum street as a wide street swept by breezes from the river. The house at the end of the row was obviously occupied by only one family. It was the same unimaginative, Victorian brick as the others, but while they were dingy, with curtains of many different types and colors at the windows, this house was freshly painted a uniform grey and the curtains were all the same white net. The door was sealing-wax red, with a highly polished brass knocker, and, on either side, were two red window-boxes, where evergreens flourished. Lit by winter sunshine, it was as dapper as a remodelled house in Beekman Place. No doubt Con Albany owned it. Though he was no longer a screen star, he must be making a decent income out of television.

Susan climbed steps above an old fashioned basement area and rang the front doorbell. Was this the way Pandora felt when she opened that box?

The grey-haired woman, who opened the door, was obviously a housekeeper. One of those informal, modern housekeepers, who thinks a red and white checked, rayon dress appropriate to the job, and who wouldn't think of wearing an apron.

"May I see Mr. Albany? I have no appointment, but it is urgent that I see him as soon as possible."

"I'm sorry, but Con is down at the studio rehearsing." There was the faintest trace of something foreign in her speech — so slight that Susan wondered if she had just imagined it. "He can't be interrupted and he won't be back until late this evening."

Susan looked at the woman more closely. "Are you Mrs. Albany?"

"Yes." Her smile was the most cheerful thing Susan had seen that day. It was a proud thing to be Mrs. Albany. "Can I help you?" She really sounded is if she wanted to help.

"Perhaps you can." Susan looked her straight in the eye. "I am Susan Lundy. Robert Lundy's wife."

How strange it was that this familiar self-introduction now brought only horror to the eyes of a stranger. It was not a proud thing to be Mrs. Robert Lundy.

"You poor child, come right in!" Susan felt a hand on her arm. She was led down a hall, cluttered with sleds and ice skates, through an archway, into a big living room that must have been made by knocking down the walls of several smaller rooms. There were windows with a river view and lots of sunshine. The furniture was old and shabby and there was no color scheme at all, but it was home-like. A home of the Nineties in some small town, inland from the Eastern Seaboard. There really should have been a Franklin stove instead of a big TV set.

"What a nice room!"

"We bought this house the year Con was in that play *Comstock Lode*. We wanted a real home, even if we had to live in New York. Then he didn't get Broadway parts any more, and there were four dreadful years when he had to commute to Hollywood by air once a week. Thank goodness, this show, *Dude Ranch*, is being shot right here in New York . . . You look all in. I'll get you tea. Or would you rather have scotch and soda? Even I have learned to drink scotch, since I've been married to Con."

"Tea, please. If it isn't too much trouble."

She came back with a tray — tea and cookies and a choice of lemon or cream. Susan took lemon and tried to eat one of the cookies, because they were obviously home-made.

Her hostess curled up in a corner of the sofa, sitting on one foot. How had a Hollywood actor, like Con Albany, who had played opposite all the famous stars in his heyday, come to marry a woman like this?

She was short and plump, with thick ankles and short, fat feet, stuffed into patent leather pumps that were too narrow for her, since there was an unsightly bulge of flesh above the edge of each shoe. Her short sleeves showed flesh sagging under the upper arm, one of the most cruel signs of age in woman. If she wore any girdle at all, it must have been an old, stretched one. Her little, round tummy was frankly on display. But the important thing about her was that, after the first moment, you did not notice any of these defects of figure at all. You were conscious only of the sweetness in her face.

It was a round face, almost child-like in its un-self-consciousness. The large, dark eyes were soft, yet they had a twinkle. This was a woman who would enjoy a good laugh, but who also knew compassion and a mother's love for the helpless and dependent. What was it that made her different from everyone else that Susan knew? After a few moments, the answer came. There was no guilt in this face. This was a woman who had nothing to reproach herself with. If she had ever done a wrong, she had done it innocently. She was either very stupid or very good . . .

"Do you want to tell me what you want to see Con about?"

"I was going to, but now . . . I don't believe I have the nerve."

"Would it be about Con's affair with Kyra Novacz?"

Susan was startled. "So you knew?"

The round face was serious, but oddly untroubled. "Of course I knew. I always know about Con's affairs with other women. When you said your husband was Robert Lundy — well, I saw the morning papers. They tell the whole story of Kyra and your husband to anyone who can read between the lines."

Susan put down her teacup. "There's no reason why I shouldn't talk to you, if you already know about Kyra and your husband. Did he tell you about . . . her?"

Mrs. Albany laughed. "Not at first, poor dear! But I'm good at reading between the lines. Con has never been able to hide anything from me."

"Do you have children?"

"Didn't you see the ice skates in the hall? We have four. The oldest is married with a baby of her own. The youngest, just twelve. And you?"

"Two. A boy, twelve; a girl, fourteen."

"That makes everything worse."

"Much worse."

The ancient freemasonry of motherhood was established between them.

"What did you want to ask Con about?"

"Mrs. Albany —"

"I wish you'd call me Elena."

Something old-fashioned in Susan usually made it hard for her to leap into first names in the first few minutes of an acquaintance, but this was one time when she felt she must do so, or feelings would be hurt.

"That's a pretty name. Elena."

"The Mexican form of Helen. You see I was a Mexican until I married Con."

That explained the trace of something foreign in her speech. Possibly it was also related to her warmth and her child-like innocence.

"Con and I went to high school together in Arizona. His folks weren't happy about me. Mexicans are second class citizens in a lot of the southwest. But —" Her chin lifted proudly. "Con married me the day after high school graduation, in spite of them, and that was thirty-one years ago. When you've known a man as long as that, he just can't hide anything from you."

"How lucky you both are to have had such a long marriage," said Susan. "What a good, old age you will both have!"

"It's the children who kept Con steady, not me," said Elena, practically. "When a man loves his children more than his wife, he stays with his wife, so the children won't be hurt by his hurting their mother. But if, in the beginning, he loves his wife more than his children, she will lose him in the end because, as everyone knows, a man's love for a woman does not last forever."

"How long have you known about Kyra and Con?"

"I've known since the first day he met her at that party for Lou Symington. When he came home, he told me all about Kyra, and I knew he had fallen for her, and I thought: 'Here we go again!' Funny thing about these girls of his. After three or four years, he can't even remember their names, or the color of their eyes, but while the thing is going on —, Oh, it's the great love of his life, he's never felt this way about a woman before and he never will again."

"This is interesting," said Susan. "It was at that same party for Lou Symington that Bob met Kyra for the first time. She must have made a play for both men and Bob never suspected. Did she see Con often after that?"

"Oh, yes, once or twice a week ever since. Did you ever read that French novel about a woman named Valerie Marneffe? A married woman, who told each of three loves that he was responsible for her pregnancy and got money from all three? Kyra was like that. A juggler of men."

Susan was beyond shock, but not beyond realizing how this would hurt Bob, if ever he learned the truth. He had sacrificed his wife and children to his belief in the integrity of Kyra's love for him. This revelation of her duplicity would break the enchanter's crystal and set him free from her spell, but would he survive the shock of such disillusion and guilt? In any case, this was not the issue at the moment. The issue now was saving Bob's life.

"Mrs. Albany — I mean, Elena — can you believe me when I tell you I am sure my husband did not kill Daniel Novacz?"

"Of course. Kyra killed Novacz. I've been sure of that all along, ever since I heard the first newscast. But how are you going to prove it?"

"I don't think anyone can ever prove that Kyra did it," said Susan, slowly. "But, if there were just a little evidence against her, it might throw some doubt on the case against Bob, so that he could not be convicted."

"How did you find out about Kyra and Con?"

"Your husband's telephone number was on the flyleaf of her address book, where she kept special unidentified numbers she wanted to hide from her husband. Bob's office number was there, too. She left the address book at our house."

"She stayed with you?" Now Elena was shocked. "Con would never have done a thing like that to me!"

Susan didn't bother to explain. She went on desperately: "Do you think your husband might know something about Kyra that would discredit her testimony?"

Elena considered. "The very fact that she was playing around simultaneously with your husband and mine wouldn't sound well in court, would it? It would reflect on her character, and so on the worth of her testimony. But you must realize that it would be quite impossible for Con to testify to anything like that. Think what it would do to his reputation! Think how it would affect his children, and his fans. *Dude Ranch* is a show for kids. The hero never kisses anyone, not even his horse!"

Susan remembered what Marienberg had said: emotional tone, suggestion, misdirection... "If Con could testify that he knew Kyra was emotionally unstable..."

"He'd still have to explain how he knew her so well. He couldn't do that."

"Does he know you know?"

"When the news of the murder was on TV yesterday, I told him I knew. I had to. I had to know if he were involved. He told me the whole story and swore that he was not involved in the crime. He insisted he hadn't seen her since last Thursday."

"The day before she came to stay with us," said Susan. "Did Con tell you anything more about her? Who her friends were and that sort of thing?"

"No. He just said he felt sorry for her having to live with that horrible husband of hers who didn't understand her."

"I thought they put it more candidly nowadays," said Susan. " 'My husband can't give me physical pleasure . . . Can you?' "

Elena smiled. "And don't forget 'I love you so much I want the whole world to know I love you' and 'I love you so much I want to bear your child.' That's the kind of thing Kyra said to Con. He told me so when he finally confessed to all this. But she did have real cause for complaint against her husband. Did you know he used to beat her?"

"She told Bob, Novacz was her father."

"That's what she told Con in the beginning. But the truth came out last Thursday."

"Did he guess?"

"No, she told him. She had to tell him then."

"Why?"

"Well, it's really quite horrible, but she wanted Con to kill her husband for her. That's when he told her that he would never see her again and I believe him, because he was frightened, really frightened, out of his wits. For fear she'd do it herself and he'd be accused. Maybe that's what happened to your husband. Maybe he refused to and then Kyra herself . . ."

"It's one line of defense, isn't it? . . . Daniel Novacz himself told me that he believed Kyra wanted to get rid of him and wanted a lover to kill him for her," said Susan. "When I saw Bob in prison, I asked him about this. He denied it. No matter what Bob feels about her accusing him in front of the police, he will not testify against her. He loved her too much to believe her capable of murder. I suppose that could mean he still loves her."

"Did he speak as if he did?"

"It's impossible to say. Prison interviews are not conducive to free communication. I felt as if I were talking to him through a thick pane of soundproof glass — just making mouths at each other without audible words at all."

"Do you think she's guilty?"

"I think that she's capable of murder, and that Bob is not."

"And yet he loves her! People in love aren't quite sane. It's like the common cold. No known cause, and no cure. You just have to wait till it's over."

Susan rose and walked to the river window, then turned to face Elena. "Do you realize that if Conrad Albany went on the witness stand and testified, under oath, that Kyra Novacz had urged him to kill her husband for her — then Bob could not possibly be convicted on the little evidence the prosecutor has against him now?"

Elena spoke, harshly:

"And do you realize that that would ruin Conrad Albany?"

"Yes, I do."

"Then you cannot ask him to do it. And you cannot ask me to ask him to do it. Fortunately for us, you cannot prove that Con knew Kyra so well."

"There's his telephone number in her address book."

"So what? She met him at a party. She wrote down his phone number. There's no evidence they saw each other again."

"Donald Tishman saw them together at the Champagne Room."

"Did he?"

"There must be other witnesses we can find, now we know what to look for."

"But there's no evidence she asked Con to kill her husband. I can deny everything I've told you today, and I shall, if I have to — even under oath. Hasn't your husband any alibi for those hours from ten to one-thirty?"

"Only an alibi unsupported by witnesses."

"What is it? Tell me?"

"After he left Kyra at a subway station, he spent twenty minutes walking towards his office. Then he decided to follow her in a taxi and spent another thirty minutes on a street corner trying to hail one in the rain. Finally, he walked to Grand Central Station, hoping to get a taxi at the cab-stand there. It was eleven-forty when he got there. A dispatcher and a policeman were on duty. Neither remembers him, though he and others had an altercation with the dispatcher, who favored passengers just off a Chicago train with hand-luggage. Twice, he almost got a cab, but the first one stalled with a dead battery and the second was pre-empted by a woman in a purple hat. He said he couldn't get ahead of her without knocking her down. He then spent a few minutes at Cobb's Corner drinking coffee, waiting for the Chicago passengers to disperse. He tried the taxi stand again. It was worse than ever. He looked at his watch and was appalled to find how much time he had wasted. It was then nearly one. He hurried outside and walked all the way to his office as fast as he could. He got there at one-thirty."

"And he never thought of taking the subway to the Novacz' apartment?"

"No. He's taxi-minded. All those men at K., K., D., and V. are. I know it's not a plausible story, but I believe it. How many of us could account for any morning in our lives plausibly? We do so many silly things we wouldn't dare do if we thought the police, or anyone else, was going to check up on us. I think Bob was in a state of indecision about a lot of things that morning — about divorcing me, about marrying Kyra, about following her to her interview with her husband, or going back to his office to wait for her call, as he had told her he would. All that was reflected in his indecisive efforts to secure a taxi. He says he was worried for fear Novacz would strike Kyra when she asked him for a divorce. But I think he was worried for fear Kyra would kill Novacz."

"Surely his lawyers will find someone who remembers seeing him at Grand Central?"

"They've tried. They haven't found anybody."

"I see. Both Kyra and Bob have motives. There are only two ways to save Bob. Either you must prove his alibi or disprove hers."

"We've tried both and we've failed both times. Remember, this murder was unpremeditated. We're not dealing with ingenious alibis confected before the fact, we're dealing with alibis that were desperately improvised after the fact. Whether they hold up, or not, is largely a matter of luck. But there may be a third way to save Bob, now." Susan sighed. "It's a pity I like you so much."

"And I like you," Elena answered. "But my husband and children come first."

"So do mine. For me." Susan rose.

"What are you going to do?" Elena was frightened now.

"What do you think? There's only one thing I can do now, isn't there?"

They stood looking at one another for a moment of silence.

"Oh, no ..." Elena's breathless words didn't break the silence — they floated upon it.

"I have no choice," said Susan. "My husband could lose his life. At the worst, all your husband could lose would be his career. For you say he can prove he was at the studio all during the crucial time."

"That's what he told me." Tears filled the warm, Latin eyes.

Susan's eyes were dry. Even her voice was dry. "So you don't quite believe him." A statement, not a question.

"I do believe him! But .... Are you going to tell this lawyer, Marienberg, all about Con and Kyra?"

"I must. It's our only chance."

And because Susan could not bear the stricken look in those dark, trusting eyes, she turned away abruptly and moved towards the hall. She was at the front door when she felt a light touch on her arm. She stopped, but she didn't look around. She could not look into those eyes again without an overwhelming sense of compassion and guilt that might unnerve her.

"Have you decided? Finally?"

"No. Not quite."

"How will I know when you decide?"

"You and Con will hear from Marienberg within ten days ... if I tell him."

"You can't. You can't do that to Con ... the children ... me. ..."

"Why not? You and I are strangers."

"But in common humanity. ..."

"I don't think I believe in common humanity any more." Susan went down the steps without looking back.

She walked towards the west. The low sun gilded the cross-town street with the melancholy tone of a dying light. She walked slowly.

What's the matter with me? Why did I say I had not decided? It's the only way to save Bob. That woman and her children are nothing to me. I have my own children to think of and their father. Where is that inner strength that I have been praying for?

But another voice in her own mind answered her: Have you the right to sacrifice these people? Is that strength? Or callousness?

She felt like an insect that has been stepped upon, still squirming, still feeling, but crushed, dying. And, in that moment of anguish, more acute than any physical pain she had ever known, her mind was suddenly clear.

I must do it, if it's the only way to save Bob. But it isn't. There is one other way. . . .

CHAPTER FOURTEEN

SINCE MARIENBERG had emphasized the importance of emotional tone in a court room, Susan took special notice of the kind of people who filled the spectators' seats to overflowing the first day of Bob's trial. She was troubled by what she saw.

They did not look like a representative cross section of the city's population. Besides the usual court room hangers-on, lawyers and their clerks, bail bondsmen, tipsters and so forth, there were a number of noticeably old people, obviously retired, those now called "senior citizens," who found time heavy on their hands. There were a few boys of high school age, in black leather jackets, one had an unlighted cigarette pasted at the corner of his lower lip, all ready to light when the bailiff was not looking. Tomorrow some principal would be asking for a written explanation of their absence from class today.

There was also a scattering of middle-aged men, who looked as if they lived on the fringes of the criminal world and probably did. Apparently, they had come in the spirit of playwrights attending another playwright's first night. Doubtless they would take a connoisseur's interest in the fine points of technique involved in both the commission of the crime and the strategy used to avoid punishment.

There were a few fashionably dressed women from the upper East Side, and a few less fashionably dressed women from the suburbs, each killing a day at a trial as they might at a *matinée*. Most of them were bored by the tedious preliminaries of court procedure and left in an hour or so. Their expressions indicated clearly that they could see much more exciting trial scenes on TV any night.

In short, the audience consisted largely of those who took a professional interest in crime, and the idle. The professionals, lawyers and criminals, would regard the whole thing as a game, with very little sympathy for the accused himself, and very little desire to see justice done. The idle — jobless, superannuated, delinquent — were all outside the main stream of life and, therefore, people who, at some level of consciousness, would be embittered. This bitterness might inspire in them a certain pleasure as they watched a man who had been as active in the main stream as Bob Lundy brought so low.

In spite of the differences in age and station, all the spectators had one thing in common. They were all capable of *schadenfreude,* the pleasure some human beings take in the suffering of others. Their spiritual ancestors had attended the Circus Maximus and watched the guillotine at work during the French Revolution.

It was a week of dull days. The harsh, electric light carved sinister shadows in the court room and brought out every physical blemish in judge and jury, lawyers and spectators, until they all looked like figures in a Daumier cartoon. What an ugly creature the human animal was in middle age! It was not a matter of baldness and lines and wrinkles that made these Daumier masks so hideous. Their real ugliness lay in the expression that breaks through the fleshy surface when the smoothness of youth is past, an expression of avidity and egoism. Someone had said that every man over forty is a scoundrel. True or not, every man and woman over forty looks like a scoundrel, thought Susan, especially by electric light.

As she listened to the district attorney's first outline of his case, she was surprised to realize how slender the evidence against Bob was. They could not place him at the actual scene of the crime at the time it took place. No one had seen him enter or leave the Novacz' apartment or the building. No one had even seen him in that neighborhood, as Susan had seen Kyra. Bob's explanation of how he had used the crucial two hours, trying to find a taxi in the rain, seemed perfectly possible to Susan. For the hundredth time, she asked herself why they had arrested Bob, instead of Kyra.

As the district attorney developed his outline, she began to understand. Though he might not have admitted it as candidly as Marienberg, he, too, attached more importance to emotional tone than factual evidence. For the prosecutor was concentrating on the one thing that had no real legal significance whatever — the motive. Bob was being tried for adultery, not for murder. He was a better target for that sort of prosecution than Kyra.

Susan sat like a woman who had been killed and stuffed, while the prosecutor informed the world, in the blandest of voices, that Robert Lundy was a man who, on the basis of the evidence, appeared to have very little moral sense in the generally accepted meaning of the words. He was a man whose job brought him into constant personal contact with Hollywood actors and actresses, who were accustomed to change their marital partners with greater freedom than other elements in the population. Apparently, Lundy had acquired their frivolous attitude towards the sanctity of the marriage tie.

He was the father of two children, a girl of fourteen and a boy of twelve. The boy had just recovered from the dread disease of polio, a circumstance that might have doubled the devotion of a normal father to his family.

"But we shall call witnesses to testify that Robert Lundy had been known to his acquaintances in New York as a philanderer for the last few years and that his affair with Kyra Novacz, widow of the deceased, was only the latest of such affairs. We will call witnesses to testify that Kyra Novacz herself was happily married to a man who had saved her from destitution in Praz, just after the war, and for whom she had the warmest feelings of gratitude... until she met Robert Lundy.

"We shall also produce testimony to prove that Mrs. Novacz was much younger and less experienced than Lundy, and that she was peculiarly vulnerable to the advances of any American, who wished to marry her, because she had a great desire to acquire American citizenship and remain in this country, where she could enjoy all the advantages of the American way of life, and she believed marriage to an American citizen would facilitate this desire. For this reason, if for no other, Robert Lundy's courtship of Kyra Novacz was more likely to succeed if he could offer her marriage.

"We shall call expert witnesses to testify that the whole history of crimes of passion shows that, when a middle-aged man is in the grip of sexual infatuation for a woman much younger than himself, his moral sense is under great pressure and there is little he will not do to keep the woman, if he is threatened with her loss. Robert Lundy had already asked his own wife for a divorce and he admits he believes she would have given it to him, if he had insisted upon it. Only the old man, Daniel Novacz, Kyra's husband, remained as an obstacle to his desire.

"It is significant that Robert Lundy cannot account for his whereabouts during the period between ten A.M. and twelve noon on the day of the crime, when, according to medical evidence and other testimony, Daniel Novacz was murdered. The prosecution maintains that Robert Lundy went to Daniel Novacz' apartment during that period and an altercation ensued, when Novacz refused absolutely to divorce Kyra, his wife, to whom he was devoted. We maintain that Robert Lundy then seized a paperweight — Exhibit A — which we shall soon show you, a heavy piece of iron, shaped like an anvil, and struck Daniel Novacz in the temple with this improvised weapon and left him for dead.

"Though it may appear that this was an unpremeditated act of rage, this appearance is not substantiated by the facts of the case. The spot where the point of the miniature anvil penetrated the temple is the thinnest place in the human skull, as medical witnesses will testify. They will show that this particular weapon might not have penetrated the skull and caused death, if any thicker spot had been chosen. Therefore, we maintain that this blow was deliberately planned and carefully calculated, with intent to kill, and we ask for a conviction of murder in the first degree."

At last, the prosecutor sat down and Susan ventured a surreptitious glance at the audience. They all looked smugly virtuous, as if they could hardly believe there actually were people in the world who committed adultery and, of course, if there were such people, murder was only the next, logical step.

They're like people at a play, thought Susan. People who sit in the audience feeling deliciously superior to the skulduggery on stage and then go to their offices the next morning and perform precisely the same sort of skulduggery themselves. Man's moral sense is peculiarly vicarious. The most brutal bully is genuinely shocked by the Nazis, and the heartless rake is sincerely appalled at the conduct of any other Don Juan. If we had the ability to see other people's sins in ourselves, it would destroy the pleasure we take in almost every play and novel that was ever written.

As it is, audiences enjoy plays about a wicked man, because it never occurs to them to identify themselves with the wicked. He is always the other fellow.

As the dull days dragged by the ordeal became an endurance test for every participant. There was a wide range of witnesses — Daniel Novacz' chief at the U.N. went on the stand to tell all he knew about Daniel and Kyra, their history and relationship. Alan Dorfmann was on the stand to give Bob's professional background. Bob's secretary and the receptionist at K., K., D., and V. testified that they had often seen Bob and Kyra together in the office and overheard a great deal of their love-making. The medical evidence was, as usual, so technical that no one understood it except the doctors. The prosecution maintained that only a man could strike the blow that killed Novacz and the defense claimed that either a man or a woman could have done so.

The inevitable psychiatrist, testifying as an expert witness, expatiated on the erotic aberrations of men of Bob's age, when hit by masculine menopause.

"Eez not joost psycholawgical," he said with a thick Viennese accent. "Eez pheesical too, weeth cawmplete invawlvment of glahndewlar seestem."

At last came the moment Susan had been dreading for days. The prosecution called Susan Lundy to the stand as a witness under subpoena.

A shortness of breath was her immediate physical reaction. At the end of each phrase, she had to stop and take another deep breath in order to go on. It was almost like drowning. She was so preoccupied with trying to hide this absurd physical reaction that she had no time or attention for any other emotions.

Yes, she had two children. Yes, Robert Lundy had asked her for a divorce in December, because he wished to marry Kyra Novacz. She herself had asked for a week to think things over. Before the week was out, Daniel Novacz had been murdered.

"Was it your impression that your husband was completely under the influence of Kyra Novacz?"

"No. My impression was that he was a man torn in two by conflicting emotions."

The prosecution did not like that answer. "But you admit that he did ask you for a divorce, Mrs. Lundy?"

"Yes."

"Does not that indicate to you that Kyra Novacz' influence over him was greater than yours?"

"It was at that particular time, yes."

"And that particular time was within forty-eight hours of the murder, was it not?"

"Yes."

The prosecution dared not go too far in the way of bullying Susan for jury and audience regarded her as a sympathetic character.

"You saw Daniel Novacz the morning of the murder?"

"Yes."

"What transpired?"

"She had said Novacz was her father. I discovered he was her husband. I asked him if he intended to divorce his wife. If he was going to refuse her the divorce, there was a chance that I might not lose my husband."

"Did he answer your question?"

"Yes. He told me he would never divorce Kyra in any circumstances whatever. He said that this was the third time she had asked him for a divorce."

The Judge intervened. "You must not testify to things he said she said."

Marienberg tried to be suave, but he could not pull in his truculent chin or take the hostility out of his voice as he objected. Hysterically, Susan thought: What a dreadful lover he would make with that voice. Every time he said "darling" it would sound like "Objection!"

"Did you meet Kyra Novacz on the street after you left her husband's apartment?"

"Yes."

"Did she say anything to you?"

"She asked me where I'd been and I told her. She asked me what Daniel Novacz had said to me and I told her that he had said he would never divorce her. She was upset."

"How did she show she was upset?"

"She ran away from me towards the apartment house. She was crying out loud: 'He must! I'll kill him, if he doesn't! I'll kill him!'"

"Mrs. Lundy, do you believe your husband is innocent?"

"I know he is. Bob is incapable of murder."

"Objection!"

"Sustained."

But she had got the point in for what it was worth. Not in the record, but in the minds of the jury. Susan, who knew Bob better than anyone else, and who had reason to be angry with him at the present time, still believed him innocent.

The superintendent of the Novacz' apartment house testified that he had called at the apartment to collect trash at eleven-thirty on the day of the murder. He had seen Kyra rush out of the apartment, and out of the building, in a state of excitement. Entering the apartment, he had seen Novacz, alive and unharmed a few moments after eleven-thirty-five. Two waiters from the Burano Restaurant testified that they had seen Kyra arrive there a minute or so before noon on the day of the crime. They knew her well, as she had lunched frequently there with Robert Lundy. It was hardly necessary to remind the jury, all New Yorkers, that she would need all of that time, from eleven-thirty-five to noon, to get from her apartment, on Riverside Drive, to the Burano in the East Thirties, even if she came by subway. So that was Kyra's alibi. On the surface it seemed unassailable.

The State called its last witness: Kyra Novacz.

She was dressed with a nun-like severity. A black dress with high neck and long sleeves, a thin edge of white outlining the roundness of the neck. A small, black *béret* was set far back on her head, like a small crown, in order to reveal the studied innocence of forehead and eyes.

Both face and voice appeared serious, candid, submissive. Had Jane Shore looked like that when she did public penance for having been a king's mistress?

How could I ever think her voice was like the voice of a child? thought Susan. It's the voice of a mechanical doll: Ma-ma . . . Da-da . . .

Kyra had dearly loved her husband, Dada Novacz. She had been swept off her feet by the romantic love-making of Robert Lundy. Tears filled her eyes. She had loved both men and now her husband was dead and her lover was arrested for the murder and it was all so horrible. But she hadn't meant any harm. She had just wanted to be happy. Never for a moment had she dreamed that Bob Lundy would do anything so violent, so reckless . . .

"Objection. Witness' opinion, not fact."

"Sustained."

"Your witness, counsellor."

Marienberg took over the questioning of Kyra.

"Is it true that, when Mrs. Lundy told you your husband would not give you a divorce, you cried out: 'He must! I'll kill him, if he doesn't! I'll kill him!' "

"That is not true. If Mrs. Lundy were not in such a highly emotional state, she wouldn't be able to imagine my saying a thing like that about my husband, whom I loved so much."

The Judge looked at Kyra with distaste. "The witness must confine herself to statements of fact and not volunteer opinions as to emotional states, or anything else."

Kyra lifted her eyelids to look up at the Bench with a slight flutter. Her voice had never been more bland. "I'm so sorry, Your Honor."

"Where did you go when you left your apartment after seeing Novacz for the last time?"

"To the Burano Restaurant."

"What did you do there?"

"I was frightened and worried. I sat alone in a booth and had two drinks. Then I called Bob Lundy at his office."

The foreman of the jury intervened for the first time. "Your Honor, the jury would like to know if this here was a dial telephone, or the old kind?"

The judge looked baffled, then gravely put the question to the witness.

"A dial telephone, Your Honor," said Kyra, looking as baffled as the judge.

"Any further questions?" asked the Judge.

"No, Your Honor." The foreman turned bright pink. "We just wanted to get the whole picture."

Susan felt sick. This man, and others like him, would decide whether or not Bob was guilty . . .

"Why did you telephone Robert Lundy?"

"I suddenly remembered I had promised him I would call him after I had seen Dada, to tell him how the interview turned out."

"Who answered the telephone?"

"I don't know. I thought then it was Bob."

"What did you say?"

"I said: 'I've got bad news, meet me for lunch at the usual time and place.' "

"I suggest that the 'bad news' was the murder of Daniel Novacz."

"But how could I know about that? I had left him alive and well."

"What was the bad news?"

"Dada's refusing me a divorce."

"Was that news to you and Mr. Lundy?"

"Yes. We had both hoped he would be generous."

"Mrs. Novacz, do you deny that thirty-six hours before the murder you urged Robert Lundy to kill your husband and Lundy indignantly refused?"

"That's a lie! A mean, wicked lie. . . ." Kyra collapsed, sobbing, and had to be excused from the stand. Marienberg said he had no further questions to ask her.

The District Attorney turned to the Judge and spoke with a full realization of his dramatic effect: "The Prosecution rests."

As the court room emptied, Susan made her way to the front where Marienberg stood talking to his assistants.

"What are our chances now?"

He was putting papers in his brief-case. He closed it and locked it before he looked up. "Bad. I'm beginning to wonder if we shouldn't have emphasized this menopause thing and tried to get a verdict of unsound mind."

"Why is it so bad?"

"Kyra Novacz' alibi for one thing. Even if Bob himself could establish a watertight alibi now, it would be hard to convict Kyra on the evidence. There just wasn't time for her to go back to Novacz' apartment after the superintendent saw him still alive and she had no logical reason for doing so."

"How much longer will the trial go on?"

"Well, I have fourteen witnesses. None of them will do us much good, but I have to go through the motions and — Yes, Wilson, what is it?"

The young clerk who had plucked at Marienberg's sleeve was excited about something. "Lady to see you, sir."

"I can't see anyone now. I'm busy."

"She said to give you this, sir." The clerk held out an envelope.

Marienberg ripped it open, took out a sheet of paper and glanced at a handwritten note. Now he was more excited than his clerk. There was a flash of the eye that was almost incandescent.

He thrust the note into his pocket. He spared only a glance for Susan. "This may change everything. Keep your fingers crossed." He turned back to the clerk. "Where is she?"

"In your office, sir."

"Let's go."

A *lady* . . . Susan stood, gazing after them. Who could "change everything" now?

CHAPTER FIFTEEN

SUSAN WOKE EARLY next morning in the New York hotel room where she had lived since the trial began. Sunshine. The first for two weeks. She hoped this was symbolic.

She lay in bed, smoking a cigarette, considering whether she should telephone Kate Trumbull and ask her to tell the children that there was hope now. Better not. The hope was too frail.

She bathed and dressed and went down to the coffee shop. A mother and two little girls were breakfasting at the next table. She watched them laughing and talking about everyday problems. My life used to be like that, an ordinary life with little problems. Shall we get a new TV set? Or shall we put the money into a dryer for the laundry? And I used to think those problems were important and difficult.

She took two aspirins with her orange juice, drank a cup

of coffee, ate half a buttered roll, and took the subway downtown to the court house.

From her seat among other spectators, she tried to study
Marienberg's face. Was it confident or dubious? She was dis-
mayed to see no trace of yesterday's excitement, but, on the
other hand, there was no look of anxiety. His face was a mask
donned to mislead opposing counsel. She had not known a
human face could be so utterly expressionless.

"My learned opponent has used all his considerable arts of
eloquence and persuasion to convince the jury that Robert
Lundy had an overwhelming motive for killing Daniel Novacz.
It is my duty to remind the jury that, however much we may
deplore some aspects of Robert Lundy's conduct, he is not
being tried on a morals charge. He is being tried for first degree
murder where the mandatory penalty is death.

"Capital punishment is too severe a penalty for adultery
and is so regarded in all civilized societies. This man's life is
at stake. He is on trial for murder and nothing else. That he
had a motive for murder is completely irrelevant in law. To
convict him, the prosecution must produce witnesses or cir-
cumstantial evidence that can place him at the scene of the
crime at the crucial time and this, we maintain, the prosecution has failed conspicuously to accomplish.

"If this jury is as intelligent as I firmly believe it to be, judg-
ing by the remarkably shrewd questions put by the foreman
to witnesses, it will ignore the emotional and moralistic overtones invoked so insidiously by the prosecution, and concen-
trate upon the only question that matters: Is there any evidence to prove that it was physically possible for Robert
Lundy to commit this murder?

"Motive is not evidence of murder. If motive led inevitably
to murder, few of us would be alive today. The law has always
recognized that the inner life of the mind is something be-

tween the individual and his God, far beyond the reach of anything as factual as evidence. The law is behaviorist. It is not interested in what a man is, but in what he does. In law the prosecution is not even required to prove motive in order to obtain a conviction of murder.

"The problem of Lundy's guilt, or innocence, is a problem of space-time, not one of morals or psychology. The prosecutor's eloquence has failed utterly to disguise the fact that he has not produced one jot or tittle of evidence to place Lundy at the scene of the crime at the time it was committed.

"And now, as new evidence has come to hand at the last moment, I must beg the court's permission to call a surprise witness to the stand."

The prosecutor was on his feet at once, wary and anxious. The two lawyers spoke to the judge in low voices for several minutes, but finally the judge ruled that the new witness could be called.

The clerk of the court raised his voice: "Elena Albany."

Susan blinked as a flashlight bulb popped almost in her face. Court attendants converged on the impudent newspaper photographer, but his grin said he didn't mind what they did to him. Hadn't he caught that look of utter astonishment on Susan Lundy's face? There might be a Pulitzer prize in it for him.

Susan's hands clenched the hoop handle of the bag in her lap. This was like one of those dreams when a character, that has no business at that particular time and place, suddenly appears, breaking all the laws of probability. She felt as helpless as if she were dreaming, too. Whatever Elena was going to say was beyond Susan's control and, worse, beyond her understanding. She could only sit and listen as passively as a tape-recorder.

The jury liked Elena at once. She was the kind of woman

that everyone likes, honest and simple. You could see it in her motherly, uncorseted figure, her warm, brown-eyed smile, her air of innocent cheerfulness. She had put on what were obviously her best clothes. A raisin silk dress, a good, dark mink cape, a necklace of good, small pearls. But the clothes that Conrad Albany's money bought her could never make her look like a woman who reads the fashion notes on the woman's page of her daily paper. Elena would always turn to the recipes and menus and, as the two women on the jury were women like her, they warmed to her immediately.

Marienberg took her through preliminaries swiftly, as if he did not want anything to diminish the shock effect of her testimony on judge or jury.

"Yes, I am the wife of Conrad Albany ... Yes, I live in New York City ..."

"Will you be kind enough to tell the jury in your own words what you were doing at ten-thirty A.M. on the day that Daniel Novacz was murdered?"

Elena turned to the jury with a beaming smile. She might have been welcoming them into her own living room or kitchen.

"Well, you see I went downtown early that morning, because there was a stocking sale at Macy's. I got a dozen nylons at half-price and then I walked crosstown. I have to have exercise, or I put on too much weight.

"I stopped for a snack at that restaurant in Grand Central Station. The one they call Cobb's Corner. I was just finishing my chocolate *éclair*, when I saw it was beginning to rain outside and I thought I'd better get a taxi, because I was wearing my feather hat and you know what rain does to feathers. The subway was no good to me, even though there is a subway station in Grand Central, because I would have to walk all the way to my home on the East River after I left the subway.

"So I went to the taxi stand in the station. You know that place where a big, neon sign says TAXIS? There were an awful lot of people there, because of the rain. I mean people from outside like me, not people just off trains. We were all trying to get taxis and I noticed this man, because he was so nice, much nicer than the other men. He didn't push or shove or try to take a taxi away from a woman, the way so many of the others did.

"And then this train came in. I think it was from Chicago. Anyway all these passengers from the train wanted to get taxis, too, and they had luggage, so the dispatcher, and the police-man hanging around, kind of favored them. The young man and I and several others argued with the dispatcher about this, but he wouldn't pay any attention to us. The man I'd noticed smiled at me and said: 'I'm going to get a cup of coffee, then I'll be back. By that time, these Chicago people will be gone.' And he was back, in about fifteen minutes. At last, an empty taxi came and I held back because the man had been there before I was, but that taxi stalled. Its battery was dead. After another wait, another empty taxi came along and he ran towards that, but a woman in a purple hat shoved him aside and jumped in. That was when he gave up. He just sort of shrugged and walked out into the street in the rain.

"I went down to the lower level to take a subway train, feather hat or no feather hat, and, as I passed the informa-tion booth, I saw that the station clock said one o'clock. I just couldn't believe that the man and I had been trying to get taxis for such a long time, but that was what the clock said."

"Did you ever see this man again?" inquired Marienberg.

"Not him, his photograph. I've been pretty busy for some time. My little Jimmy had measles real bad and we all know what that's like. So I didn't even glance at a newspaper for quite a while. But, yesterday morning, Jimmy was so much better, that I took a little time off to have a second cup of coffee after breakfast and read the newspaper that Con had left on his chair, when he went to the studio.

"It was the *Daily News* and the first thing I saw was this big picture of this man on the front page. I mean, the man I'd seen at Grand Central. If it hadn't been such a big picture, I might not have recognized him, but it covered the whole front page and, when I turned the page to read about him, it said he was being tried for a murder committed last December 6th.

"I thought then: why it was just about two weeks before Christmas that I saw him at Grand Central! The paper said he had no alibi, so I went to his lawyer and the lawyer called Macy's and found out that their only stocking sale last December was on the 6th, the day of the murder."

"Mrs. Albany, do you see that man in court now?"

"Oh, yes, Mr. Marienberg! He's right over there." Elena pointed to Bob.

Susan closed her eyes and told herself that she must not faint. All around her she could hear the roar of excited voices like a storm at sea.

She sat still. It seemed a long time before young Wilson, Marienberg's clerk, forced his way through the crowd to her side. "You look like death," he said. "I'm going to get you out of here."

Docile, she followed as he forced a path for her through the crowd. Most of the reporters were around Elena and Marienberg, but one reporter caught her by the sleeve. "Any comment, Mrs. Lundy?"

The honest joy and relief in his voice moved her so deeply that she began to feel alive again. "Just say that this has made me very happy."

Wilson pushed the reporter aside indignantly, and pulled her through a gap in the crowd. She leaned on his arm as they went downstairs.

"I'd like to thank Mrs. Albany."

"You'll have a chance, later. Now stay right here, by this door, and I'll get you a taxi."

A gust of fresh air came through the door as he opened it, warm air that reminded her this was spring. She took a deep, grateful breath. Life was beginning again. It was a happy yet painful process, like restoring circulation to an arm that has been in a tourniquet too long.

Wilson was back. "Here's your cab. Lucky it wasn't raining today!"

She laughed too loudly, on the edge of hysteria.

"The driver will take you to our office to wait for Mr. Lundy. He should be released pretty soon, I think. The prosecution has thrown in its hand." A thought struck the boy. "You do want to see your husband, don't you?"

"Yes, oh, yes!"

Again Susan was shown into the reception room with all the photographs of Marienberg. She smoked every cigarette in her case and it seemed to her as if years passed before she heard a step in the corridor outside. Bob? Absurdly, she felt a sudden shyness about meeting him here and now. What could they say to each other after all this?

But it was Elena.

She came in smiling. "They said you wanted to thank me."

"How can I? What you did was fantastic and heroic. I can't believe it! And you never gave me a hint that you were going to do it."

"Of course not. You're not an actress. You never could have faked that look of utter astonishment when I was called to the stand. It's on record, too. A newspaper photographer took a flash-picture of you at that moment. No one, including Marienberg, will ever guess you had anything to do with Bob's alibi."

"How did you find the nerve to do it? Do you know the penalties for perjury?"

But Elena only laughed. "What else could I do in the circumstances? I couldn't let Con go on the stand and testify about Kyra's talk of killing her husband without hurting him and his career, his children and me. But that one, little bit of testimony might have thrown enough reasonable doubt on the case against Bob to save his life. How could I stand by and see a nice man, like your husband, die in order to spare my husband? And all for a woman like Kyra! I couldn't."

Susan glanced towards the door uneasily. "Does Marienberg suspect? Or Bob?"

"How can they? The big lie is always believed. How could I know all those details of Bob's alibi, which he had already told Marienberg and you? It wasn't in the papers, because the defense had not yet presented its case. I knew only because you told me, but no one, including Bob and Marienberg, has the slightest idea that we have ever met before today. Marienberg doesn't even know our husbands ever met. And, thank God, Marienberg knows nothing about Con's relations with Kyra. When my story matched Bob's so perfectly in every detail, Marienberg had to believe it was true. And his sincere belief that I was speaking the truth, and that Bob Lundy was innocent, had a great deal to do with his being able to convince the judge and jury that Bob was innocent."

"How can I thank you?"

"I have something to thank you for. You could have told Marienberg to go after Con and force him to testify because Con was also Kyra's lover and, theoretically, he also had a motive for murdering Novacz. But you didn't. You came to me instead and, after you heard my story, you left us in peace."

"I suppose I didn't believe that ruining your husband would save mine. Perhaps . . . if I had. . . ."

"You would have done it? I understand. But I'm glad you didn't. This way is so much better. No one is hurt."

"Except Kyra, if they indict her now. Will they?"

"Who knows? Who cares? We know she must be guilty!"

"Elena, no man would have done what you did. Men have too much respect for law."

"But I am not a man! Why should I behave like one? You know another reason I did this? You had such faith in your man. It deserved to be rewarded. But now . . . there is only one thing that bothers me. . . ."

"And that is?"

Elena's voice faltered, as if her talk with Susan had hobbled the generous impulse that had carried her so far in Bob's defense. As if she suddenly realized the enormity of what she had done.

"I hope your faith in him is justified, because, if it isn't . . . from now on you'll be living with a murderer."

CHAPTER SIXTEEN

A MONTH BEFORE the next Christmas, Susan got
out the wreaths of evergreen with their little, shiny balls, red
and silver and blue, and their doves, white as birds moulded
in snow. Bob helped her hang the red wreath from the brass
knocker outside, where it looked festive against the pale, blue
door. Over the fireplace, they hung the blue wreath, and in
the big front window, the silver wreath.

On the dining table, the bowl for cut flowers was replaced
by a miniature Christmas tree that stood on a small silver
music box. When it was wound up, the little tree revolved
slowly and the box played *God Rest Ye Merry, Gentlemen.*
The Sheffield candlesticks on the piano were gay with red
candles and Christmas *bobèches* — little glass saucers to catch
melting wax, each decorated with a miniature Christmas
wreath of its own.

Buzz had left his transistor radio going on the window-sill. Already daytime disc jockeys were playing Christmas carols. The nostalgic music brought back all their other Christmases together. The first one after they were married, when they were still living in New York. The first one in this house, when Robin was only two months old. Buzzy's first Christmas, a year later, when he was three weeks old and Robin was just learning to walk and talk.

"Well, that's about it," said Bob, looking around living room and dining room.

"Oh, no! There's one more thing."

Every Christmas, since they had been in this house, there had always been a branch of mistletoe over the door from the hall into the living room. It was always Bob's task to hang that, for Susan couldn't reach the hook without a ladder and Bob could.

She stood looking up at him and, when the mistletoe was in place, he turned to look down at her. For a moment neither of them could speak. Then he leaned down to kiss her. She dropped her eyelids so he couldn't see tears — he hated tears. She said: "There was a time when I thought we would never put up these things together again."

His arm was around her shoulders. He said: "Don't think about it now. And I always loved you even when I loved her most. There was always one corner of my mind that knew I had made a wrong decision, but I'd decided what I was going to do, so I had to go through with it. Just like having a dream that is very real to you, and yet, in one corner of your mind, you know all the time that it's just a dream. That's what no one else will ever understand. That's what I don't understand myself."

"I think I understand," said Susan. "There are many different kinds of love and unfortunately one does not exclude the others."

A voice from the radio cut across their thoughts.

"... Lou Symington's divorce from Dick Grant. Interviewed at the Waldorf hotel in New York, where she is staying, Miss Symington declared: 'I have never known love before, but this is The Real Thing.' She and Barry Norton will be married just as soon as he gets back from Las Vegas with a divorce from his third wife, Mabel Wells, the clothespin heiress...."

"I wonder what became of Kyra?" said Susan.

"I couldn't care less," answered Bob. "The whole thing seems remote now, as if it had all happened to someone else, not to me. But one thing I can never forget: that awful moment in Dorfmann's office, when Kyra cried out in front of the police: 'Oh, Bob, how could you kill poor, dear, old Dada, when you knew I loved him so much!' Even in court she made it sound as if I were guilty. How could she? She must have known I was innocent since she was the murderer herself."

"She was never arrested."

"Lack of evidence, I suppose. She must have gone back to Novacz' apartment for a few minutes after the superintendent saw her leave the first time, but there were no witnesses, so the police couldn't prove it. I wonder if they ever will...."

Through the big window, they could see Robin and Buzz building a snowman on the lawn below the open terrace. Their cheeks were bright pink from the cold in spite of wool slacks and mittens and nylon windbreakers, but they were laughing and Buzz was no longer wearing braces.

"I'm going to help." Bob reached for his jacket, paused to look at Susan. "To think that I nearly lost them.... And we'll only have them for a few years longer. Before we know it, they'll be grown up and gone away. How easily I might have missed these last, few, irreplaceable years . . ."

Susan sat down at her desk to make out their Christmas shopping list. The desk was near the window, overlooking the terrace and the snowy field that sloped down to the frozen brook. The sky was a tender, baby blue, the new-fallen snow still a clean white and the whole scene was washed with the pale yellow of winter sunshine.

She sat for a few moments, watching. Bob was rolling a snowball down the slope, gathering more snow on the way to form the snowman's top-heavy head. Buzz was working on one of its arms. Robin was packing snow against the embryo snowman's stomach, so he would have a paunch like Santa Claus'. Those three were her whole world and she had come so near to seeing that world smashed that, even now, the thought could bring a shiver to her spine, if she dwelt for any length of time on the danger that had passed.

Don't think about it now. It's all over. We're safe. We're together again.

She looked at the balance in her checkbook. She wanted to buy three really nice presents this year, but there wasn't too much money. Selling insurance and real estate on commission in the country was not as profitable as working for K., K., D., and V. in New York. The people of Abingdon had been kind to Bob after his acquittal. They had made a place for him in the local business world when they didn't really need him, and his new life relieved him of the physical strain of commuting. Perhaps now Buzz was entirely well, she should try to get back her old job as a primary school teacher. Small as the salary was, it would help pay off the loan, and, before long, even school boards would have forgotten the association of the name Lundy with scandal and violence . . .

She began to write down her list. Bob . . . electric razor? The new kind with floating heads? Buzz . . . a watch. Surely he was past the watch-losing age now . . . And Robin? . . . Clothes, of course. They were all she wanted now. How about that winter coat, lined with rabbit fur, she had admired in the shop window downtown? Robin could never pay for it out of her dress allowance . . .

Outside the window, they were fitting the head onto the snowman. Susan lost herself again in the sheer pleasure of watching them. And it was then that the radio voice cut across her thoughts once more:

". . . among those sailing on the Green Star ship, *Moldavia*, for Hamburg today, was Kyra Novacz, who figured in the news last spring, when Robert Lundy of Abingdon, New York, was tried for the murder of her husband, Daniel Novacz, and acquitted. As there was insufficient evidence to indict anyone else, the killing of Daniel Novacz remains one of the few unsolved murder cases in the annals of the New York Police Department.

"At the pier today, Mrs. Novacz refused to be interviewed, but a representative of her country's delegation to the U.N., which employed her late husband, saw her off at the pier and told reporters that Mrs. Novacz was returning to her own country after months spent under psychiatric care.

" 'Our delegation to the U.N. has no job to offer Mrs. Novacz,' he said. 'But she will be provided for at home. In our country we always provide generously for widows of distinguished public servants and our government has arranged employment for Daniel Novacz' widow on one of our collective farms, where it is hoped that outdoor work and a wholesome, country atmosphere will do a great deal to restore her mental health, which was so rudely shattered by the ordeal of her husband's murder. . . .' "

Susan switched off the radio.

So it really was all over.

She buried her face in her hands as memories came flooding back.

...*He must! I'll kill him if he doesn't!* ... Kyra, screaming and running away through the rain. Susan moving on, in the other direction, then pausing. Suppose she does kill him? What will that mean to Bob, to the children, to me?

Susan turning, walking back towards the Novacz' apartment house. No sign of Kyra, but the front door of the building ajar.... Susan stepping inside, closing the door behind her, knocking on the door of Novacz' apartment....

Daniel Novacz opening the door, alone, facing her with tormented eyes....

"Has Kyra been here?"

"Yes."

"And you told her ... ?"

"That I would never give her a divorce? Yes. She ran out in tears, but ... Oh, Mrs. Lundy...."

His face was working.

"Well? What?"

"I am more fond of Kyra than I thought and I cannot stand her tears now.... I keep seeing her as I first saw her. A young girl, almost a little girl; torn, dirty clothes; terror in her eyes. ... I am old. There is no way I can provide for her future, but your husband could. So I have changed my mind. I must find Kyra quickly and tell her that she can have her divorce after all. I shall give her up...."

It was like an explosion — that blinding, burning flash of rage and the roaring in her ears. Her hand closed over something on the desk. She didn't see then that it was a paperweight shaped like an anvil. She didn't strike him with it — she hurled it at him. The maudlin, senile fool, who had just said he was preparing to ruin her happiness (and her children's) for the sake of a woman like Kyra — a liar, a cheat, a thing who used womanhood to destroy children, not to nurture them. . . .

The paperweight might have missed him altogether. It might have struck harmlessly against his arm or shoulder. But the point buried itself in his temple and he went down with the thing still imbedded in his skull.

There were no bloodstains on her. She had been standing too far away from him when she threw the thing.

She knew instantly that he was dead. Only then did it come to her: In destroying him, she had destroyed Kyra, too. Only Kyra and Bob had a motive for killing Novacz and Bob had an alibi. Bob was in his office this morning, Kyra had just said. So no one, not even Kyra, could know that Susan had a motive, too. She and Novacz were the only ones who knew that Novacz had changed his mind about giving Kyra a divorce, and he was dead. Killed, ironically enough, for what was probably the only generous act in his whole life.

If Susan had killed Kyra, everyone would have suspected her. Her motive was obvious and overwhelming in the classic tradition of the crime of passion. But who would suspect her of killing Novacz, when she had every reason for keeping Novacz alive as the chief obstacle to Bob's marrying Kyra? And now, if she killed Kyra by letting Kyra be executed for Novacz' murder, who would suspect that? Kyra was sure to be the one accused; Bob had an alibi. . . .

Susan had not planned it that way, but it had happened that way. And now what should she do? Give herself up to the police to spare Kyra, who was threatening to destroy her children's happiness, and her own? Or let the destroyer be destroyed. . . .

Susan had told Kate Trumbull that she, Susan, was a less nice person since Kyra came into her life. What kind of person was she really now?

In less than an hour, she learned that the choice was not to be a clear-cut moral issue between herself and her worst enemy. Bob was not in his office at the time of the murder. He had no alibi. Kyra had been mistaken.

That shock brought her to her senses again. If it ever came to the point, she could not let Kyra die for a murder Kyra had not committed. She had no compassion for Kyra, but she had compassion for herself. She could not let Kyra's evil nature turn her, Susan, into a nature equally evil. That would have been final victory for Kyra, perhaps the greatest victory Kyra could possibly have.

Should she confess immediately to spare Bob the long-drawn torture of trial? Or should she work for his acquittal, hoping that she would not have to confess, because no one else could be convicted of her crime? What would Bob himself want her to do, if he knew the truth?

There was no one she could ask. It would be impossible to tell Bob during one of those ghastly, guarded interviews in prison, and she didn't like, or trust, Marienberg. She had to make her decision alone. It would have been a relief to confess and get it over with, but what of the children then? They would have lost both parents, they could have been proud of neither one. As long as there was a chance that Bob would be acquitted and Kyra never accused, let the children believe that their mother was still the woman they had always known, let Bob himself believe that Susan was one of the solid things in a world where so much was shifting and shadowy. She could always save Bob by confessing at the last moment, if it came to the point.

Her own guilt was the weapon she held always in reserve to use if all else failed. Because of that, she had been compelled to spare Conrad Albany. She knew, only too well, that he was not guilty of murder, and she could not sacrifice an innocent man's career when there was still another way to save Bob — by sacrificing herself, the real murderer. But she had been spared that, because she had spared Elena, and Elena was a woman who paid her debts.

Thank God. . . .

She got up and put on her warm coat and mittens and went out into the snow and the sunshine, to the three people she loved most in the whole world.

THE END